COMPOUND
LOCOMOTIVES
OF THE
BRITISH ISLES

COMPOUND
LOCOMOTIVES
OF THE
BRITISH ISLES

Tom Pearce-Carr

FINIAL PUBLISHING

First published 2007 by
FINIAL PUBLISHING

ISBN 978-1-900467-37-7

Produced by Finial Publishing
15 Abingdon Drive, Caversham Park, Reading, Berks RG4 6SA, England
Tel/Fax: 0118-9484103
www.finial.co.uk
www.finial.ndirect.co.uk
Email: mail@finial.co.uk

To:
Arthur Taylor Armstrong 1887 - 1959
"An inspiration to learn"

Foreword

Railways are truly in my blood. My Maternal Great Grandfathers were both engine fitters for the North Eastern Railway at Gateshead as was one of my Great, Great Grandfathers. He worked for the Railway for over 60 years.

My earliest memories are of standing with my Grandfather, to whom this book is dedicated, watching the trains at Newcastle Central. Later, when the family moved to London, I became one of the regulars in the group at the end of Platform 10 at Kings Cross. A further move took me to a country station between Exeter and Barnstaple in North Devon, where I learned the intricacies of the bell codes and token exchanges of the signal box and was welcomed onto the footplate of the daily goods while it shunted in the yard. Trips into Barnstaple were often taken on the footplate of a Bullied 'Light Pacific', Drummond 'T9' or 'M7' or a Maunsell 'Mogul'. Thus did my passion grow over the years and a few months as a Cleaner in my 'gap year' did nothing to dampen it.

So why a book about 'Compounds'? I always thought that despite the efforts of Churchward, Gresley, Bulleid *et al*, the full potential of the British steam locomotive was not exploited. In France, the work of Chapelon showed what could be done with a modern compound and it is a real shame that no one took the same path on this side of the Channel.

This book took many years to write and even longer to publish and some thanks are due. Firstly to my wife who pushed me into finishing it, secondly to John Villers of Finial Publishing, who we met on the platform of Wooda Bay station on the Lynton & Barnstaple and who offered his help. To the North Eastern Railway Museum at Darlington for the NER photographs and to the Staff of the Public Records Office at Kew for the photographs of the Webb compounds and finally to all the railwaymen who have patiently shared their experiences with me over the years.

Contents

Introduction

From the moment that the first lumbering steam locomotives began to trundle their loads of coal along the wagon-ways of the North of England, railway engineers looked for ways to make the new machine more efficient. At first, of course, it was more a matter of making them work at all, rather than worrying about such matters as fuel consumption. The steam engine was first put into a chassis to run on rails by Richard Trevithick, the 'Cornish Giant' in 1803 and he ran into the problem which was to plague locomotive engineers for the next one hundred and fifty years. His engine was too heavy for the track.

In principle, the steam engine is very simple; a boiler is fitted to turn water into steam. A conventional locomotive boiler consists of a cylinder with two end plates. Between these plates run tubes which carry the hot gases from the fire-box to the chimney. During their passage through the tubes, some of the heat is transferred to the water to produce steam. The fire-box is fitted within the rear of the boiler and is surrounded by water spaces and in these spaces metal stays are fitted to brace the box against the steam pressure. In the bottom of the box are dampers, or air spaces, which admit air through a grate on which the coal is burned. An important factor is the area of this grate, because to some extent this is an indication of the amount of coal which the locomotive can burn and so a measure of the power output available. Early locomotives burned coke because this was almost smokeless and burned quickly. Coal requires a slower combustion and a larger box with a longer route to the boiler for the gases to be completely burned, a deflector made up of a brick arch is usually fitted to achieve this end. Boiler development went along hand-in-hand with the engine 'works'. The early days of hand riveted, wrought iron boilers, made up of several small plates, were followed from the 1890s, by steel boilers, rolled from large plates and capable of taking working pressures of up to 200p.s.i.

Steam is collected at the highest point in the boiler and fed through a regulator, or throttle valve, to the engine part of the locomotive. It must then be converted into motion and to do this a piston is driven from one end of a cylinder to the other by the pressure of the steam. This to-and-fro motion is taken by a connecting rod to a crank on the driving axle and so converted to a revolving one at the wheel. It is necessary to have some means of admitting the steam at the start of the stroke and exhausting it at the other end of the cylinder. This device is the valve gear. In the early stationary engines of Watt and Newcomen, the driver worked the valve gear manually, but as speeds increased, this became impossible and the operating rods for the gear were attached to the piston rod. The valves were usually in the shape of the letter 'D' laid on its side and these slid back and forth uncovering holes, or ports, in the ends of the cylinder casting, alternately admitting and exhausting steam at each end of the piston stroke. Thus, the piston was driven for the full length of its stroke by steam taken directly from the boiler. Even at the low pressures of the early days, when 50p.s.i. was normal, the steam came out of the exhaust pipe with great force and with lots of noise. This was unimportant on the private colliery lines, but once the railways began to run in public, some means had to be found to make them quieter. It is probable that this resulted, by chance, in a very important development. The exhaust was directed up the chimney to act as a silencer and it was discovered that the flow of steam drew the fire and made it burn much more fiercely, an effect called the 'blast pipe'. By 1816, George Stephenson was using an eccentric to drive the valve rods and, by fitting two eccentrics in different positions on an axle, either forward or backward motion could be selected. It was soon realised that the efficiency of the engine could be greatly improved if the steam could be expanded to a lower pressure before it was exhausted into the atmosphere and this led to the development of valve gears to allow 'expansive' working. This means that the admission from the boiler can be 'cut off' at some point in the piston stroke and the piston is then driven for the rest of its stroke by the expansion of the steam. Because the exhaust point has to be constant, a simple motion will not do the job. The feature of all expansion gears is that they require a drive to be taken from two points to combine the motion imparted to the valves. There are three designs of valve gear which we shall meet in the course of this book which achieve these requirements by different means. They are the Howe = Stephenson Link Motion, Walschaerts Radial Gear and David Joy's Radial Gear.

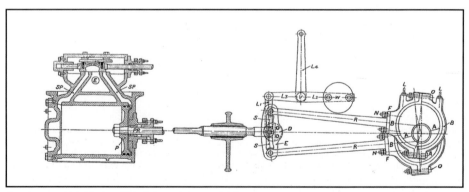

Stephenson Link Motion. This link motion was the first to be designed to replace the old 'Gab' motion and allow expansive working by means of variable cut off. The movement is obtained from two eccentrics, 'A', on the driving axle and carried by the radius rods, 'R', to the slotted link 'S'. Variation in cut off and reversing is accomplished by raising and lowering the link by means of the lifting arm, 'L'.

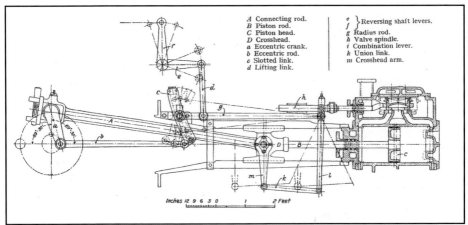

A Connecting rod.
B Piston rod.
C Piston head.
D Crosshead.
a Eccentric crank.
b Eccentric rod.
c Slotted link.
d Lifting link.

e } Reversing shaft levers.
f }
g Radius rod.
h Valve spindle.
i Combination lever.
k Union link.
m Crosshead arm.

Walschaerts Radial Valve Gear. With this type of gear the motion for the valves is obtained from a combination of levers which are actuated by an eccentric or return crank, 'a' and a connection to the crosshead, 'm', 'k' and 'i'. The amount of lap and lead is directly controlled by the combination lever and the motion for opening and closing the valves from the eccentric or return crank, The slotted link oscillates about the fixed centre which holds it in position according to the setting of the return crank relative to the dead centre positions. Reversing is carried out by raising or lowering the slotted link above or below the fixed centre thus raising or lowering the radius rods.

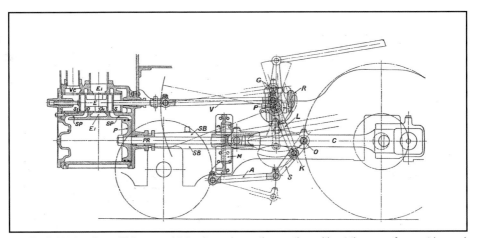

Joy Radial Valve Gear. This gear obtains its reciprocating motion without the use of eccentrics and so allows room for a substantial increase in the strength of the crank webs and width of the driving axle bearings in inside cylinder locomotives. It offers a reduction in working parts, constant valve lead and good steam distribution. The necessary reciprocating movement is obtained from the connecting rod, 'C'. At a point about one third of the rod from the small end, a hole, 'O', usually about 3in. diameter is bored and fitted with a bush, to which is attached the stirrup link, 'S', This link is connected at its other end to an anchor link 'A' which is anchored to a fixed point on the motion plate, 'M'. At 'K' the stirrup link is connected to the swing links 'L" the top ends of which are attached to the valve rod, 'V'. The swing links are bored at point 'P' and a pin is fitted which carries the slipper blocks working in curved guides, 'G', inserted and secured into the reversing shaft, 'R'.

Three terms which we shall meet in this book which refer to valve movement are 'lead', 'lap' and 'valve travel'. Because the physical movement of steam in and out of a cylinder is not instantaneous, time must be allowed in the valve motion for the process. So, the admission valve opens a little before the piston reaches the end of its stroke and, at the other end of the cylinder, the exhaust opening also anticipates. This allowance is called the 'lead'. The 'lap' of a valve is that amount by which it overlaps the ports when in the middle of its travel. By increasing the amount of lap and at the same time increasing the total valve travel, it is possible to use an earlier point of cut-off without restricting the amount by which the steam port is opened. As boiler pressures increased towards the end of the nineteenth century, largely as the result of the use of steel boilers, engineers became concerned at the frictional losses incurred in driving slide valves and began to experiment with the use of piston valves. Piston valves, as the name implies, run in a cylinder rather than over a flat surface. This results in much less friction, although problems of leakage and lubrication were not wholly solved until very late in the history of steam locomotives.

As speeds and the weight of trains increased, the cost of fuel, particularly on those railways relatively remote from the coal fields, began to reach levels which rang alarm bells in the minds of those out to keep their dividends as high as possible. The efficiency of any steam engine depends largely upon the amount of energy which can be extracted from the steam in its passage through the cylinders. Thus, the greater the difference between the entry pressure and the exhaust, then the greater the efficiency. In stationary and marine applications, this can be increased by exhausting the steam into a condenser at a pressure below that of the atmosphere but, in the case of a steam locomotive, some residual pressure is necessary in order to produce the blast on the fire to make it burn hot enough to keep up the boiler production. The relatively low boiler pressures of the early days, together with the valve gears in use, made the difference, or ratio of expansion, small. A solution was to expand the steam successively in two cylinders and so extract more work from it before exhausting it into the air. This system is called 'compounding' and its application in Britain is the subject of this book.

The compound locomotive originated on the Eastern Counties Railway. As early as 1850, a patent was taken out by James Samuel, who was the resident engineer of that railway. However, credit for the invention is usually given to John Nicholson, an employee in the locomotive department. Their collaboration resulted in the re-building of two existing locomotives, both 2-4-0s, as two-cylinder compounds. The system differed from that used in later compound locomotives in that they were 'continuous expansion' engines and the steam was expanded simultaneously in the two cylinders. The two cylinders were of different sizes, in the ratio of volume of 1:2.3 and the cranks were set at 90-degrees. Live steam was admitted to the smaller, high-pressure cylinder and the cut-off was set at 50%. At this point, a slide valve operated by a fifth eccentric opened, allowing some of the steam to flow to the larger, low-pressure cylinder which was just beginning its stroke. From this point onwards, expansion continued in both cylinders.

About 44% of the steam was retained in the high-pressure cylinder and exhausted at a pressure of 30p.s.i., while that in the low-pressure side was taken as low as possible, about 5p.s.i., before being released. It was thought that the higher pressure exhaust would be necessary to maintain an adequate blast on the fire.

Because in any two-cylinder compound locomotive, there are points in the piston stroke where the high-pressure cylinder cannot exert enough force to start, a special system was needed for starting. This took the form of a simple valve, under the control of the driver, to admit live steam to the low-pressure cylinder for starting and also when additional effort was needed while running.

The original patent mentions a boiler pressure of 160p.s.i., but in the case of the rebuilt locomotives, the old iron boilers were retained and the pressure was 110p.s.i. The fear that the blast would be insufficient to maintain the pressure led to one of the locomotives retaining the original 15in. x 24in. cylinders and so this further precluded a fair trial. Nevertheless, a fuel saving of 12lbs. of coal per mile was claimed. This was probably a comment as much on the inefficiency of the original engines, as any inherent improvement in the system itself. The efficiency was bound to suffer as a result of the 44% of the steam on the high-pressure side being exhausted at the same temperature as that in a simple engine. The system was afterwards used with some success in stationary applications. A more conventional two-cylinder system was adopted by T. W. Wordless, first on the Great Eastern and then with more success on the North Eastern. In this case, the steam was exhausted from the high-pressure cylinder at the end of its stroke through a receiving pipe and directly to the inlet side of the low-pressure valve. A simple hand valve was fitted for starting, but more complicated arrangements came later. Because of the limitations of the loading gauge, it was difficult to fit a large enough low-pressure cylinder and the work was shared unevenly with the high-pressure side doing more than its fair share. To get over this problem, Wordsell arranged the valve events to give a later cutoff in the low-pressure cylinder. Unfortunately, this made the engine awkward to handle when shunting or running backward, as in reverse the cut-off was later in the high-pressure side.

F. W. Webb introduced his three-cylinder system on the London & North Western Railway in which two outside high-pressure cylinders exhausted into a single large low-pressure one between the frames. Several hundred were built for both passenger and freight haulage. The passenger locomotives had uncoupled driving wheels. They were moderately successful, but temperamental power units.

At the end of his career, Webb developed a four-cylinder system, which suffered from unbalanced volume ratios resulting in sluggish performance.

On the North Eastern Railway, the Chief Draughtsman, W. M. Smith, also designed a three-cylinder system, but this time it was the other way round, that is with one, inside, high-pressure cylinder and two low-pressure ones outside. The North Eastern built only one such locomotive, but the design was copied by the Midland and later the LMS and these eventually became the most numerous of the British compounds.

Other railways also built locomotives to one or other of these systems and both the North British and the Great Western produced four-cylinder tandem compounds without notable success.

In view of the extensive use of compounds on the Continent, particularly in France, it is a great pity that none of the designs of the 1920s were built in this country. Notable among these were the Fowler 'Pacific' and an idea put forward by Stanier to Collett at Swindon for a compound 'Castle'. This was apparently dismissed in about thirty seconds flat! Thus, the chance to see whether a really modern compound, with high boiler pressure, high superheat and a modern valve gear would have had the better of the more simple designs produced was lost.

Chapter 1

London & North Western Railway

In 1878, Antonole Mallet displayed the first two-cylinder compound tank engine at the Paris Exhibition. Webb was impressed by the principle and proceeded to convert one of the old Allan-Trevithick 2-2-2 locomotives. No.54 *Medusa*, renumbered 1874, by lining up the left-hand cylinder to 9in. The bore of the other cylinder was kept at 15in. and the stroke of both was 20in. Boiler pressure was 140p.s.i. The *Medusa* had the Mallet system of manual valves for starting, which allowed the driver to work the locomotive as a two-cylinder simple when required. It was set to work on the Ashby to Nuneaton branch and, with the experience thus gained, Webb was convinced that the future of North Western locomotive operation should be largely compound.

Francis William Webb was an out and out North Western man. He had been a pupil of Francis Trevithick at Crewe from 1851 and had risen through the post of Chief Draughtsman to be Chief Assistant to John Ramsbottom ten years later. In 1866, he left the railway to become manager of the Bolton Iron & Steel Company. When Ramsbottom retired in 1871, Webb was appointed Chief Mechanical Engineer at Crewe. According to John Marshall in 'A Biographical Dictionary of Railway Engineers', he was "a severe, autocratic and intolerant man. He never married and made few friends. He made a large amount of money, most of which he gave or bequeathed to charities. His erratic temper and manner eventually led to his enforced retirement in 1904".

Webb is best remembered for his compounds, but it must be said, they represented only a few hundred of the over 4,000 locomotives built at Crewe during his career. In contrast to the compounds, his simple designs were extremely long-lived. Many survived the ruthless standardisation of the LMS days and worked onto the 1950s. The famous racer of 1898, *Hardwick* still survives to show the modern enthusiast the neat, practical outline of a Victorian locomotive.

In the thirteen years between his appointment and the first compound, Webb had established a solid basis of engineering excellence, both in the workshop and locomotive practice of the London & North Western. He enlarged and improved the works at Crewe and imported new men and ideas. The Wordsell brothers, whose works are referred to elsewhere in this book, were among these. After this period of consolidation, it is not surprising that his mind should turn towards more innovative designs. Operating costs were rising and any method of improving efficiency was bound to receive the support of a Board of Directors looking for higher profits. This method, to Webb in 1879, was compounding.

It was Webb's original intention that his three-cylinder compounds should have the same cylinder arrangement as that later adopted by W. M. Smith i.e. two outside low- pressure cylinders and one inside high-pressure. In the discussion that followed Mallet's paper on compounding to the Institute of Mechanical Engineers in 1879, Webb declared his intention to "get a compound locomotive which would work steadily and economically at high speeds" and that "it would be necessary to go back in form to the engine by R. Stephenson having three cylinders. The boiler steam should be taken to the middle cylinder first, and thence into the outside cylinders, which should have their cranks in the same position and at right angles to the crank of the middle cylinder". The Stephenson locomotive referred to had been built for the Newcastle & Darlington Junction Railway by Robert Stephenson & Co. in 1852 and the unusual crank arrangement was adopted in order to achieve smooth running. As the two outside cylinders worked in unison, there were no unbalanced reciprocating forces and any swaying or 'nosing' from side to side, so noticeable in such locomotives as Ramsbottom's 'Lady of the Lake' class, was totally eliminated. However, in the event, neither the crank, or the cylinder arrangements were adopted. Ahrons could find no official explanation for the change from the original design, other than a quotation from the proceedings of the Institute of Civil Engineers in 1888, when Mr. Edgar Worthington suggested that the uneven pressure produced in the low-pressure receiver by the single high-pressure cylinder may have been the reason.

A single locomotive, *Experiment*, was built in January 1882 to test the three-cylinder principle in main line passenger work. This was a 2-2-2 with inside frames; the leading axle was of Webb's radial design and the two rear axles carried uncoupled driving wheels. The outside, high-pressure cylinders, 11½in. in diameter, drove the rear axle and the single, inside, low-pressure cylinder, 26in. in diameter, the leading driving axle. The common stroke being 24in. Joy radial valve gear actuated the slide valves, which were underneath the high-pressure cylinders and on top of the low-pressure; this allowed the high-pressure valves to fall from their seats when steam was shut off. High-pressure steam was carried in a 3in. pipe on each side, which ran inside the smokebox, through the back plate and between the frames to the valve chests. The high-pressure exhaust returned by the same route; this time in two 4in. pipes, which were carried almost to the top of the smokebox, crossed over and thence into the low-pressure valve chest with ports 14in. x 1½in. The purpose of this was to provide some re-heating of the steam between the high-pressure and low-pressure cylinders. The exhaust, only two beats per revolution, of course, was carried through a blast pipe 4⅝in. in diameter.

The boiler was interchangeable with that of the 'Precedent' class simples, having a tube heating surface of 980sq.ft. and 1,03.5sq.ft. provided by the firebox, making a total of 1,083.5sq.ft. and a grate area of 17.1sq.ft. The firebox was fitted with a water bottom, which was not included in the heating surface on these locomotives, although it was in later classes. This feature of the design had originated on some earlier goods engines and was supposed to aid the water circulation. A contemporary writer doubted the efficiency of the increased surface, as he had seen ice formed on the outside of the space after a winter run. The boiler pressure was raised from the 140p.s.i. of the simples to 150p.s.i. The leading wheels, 3ft 7in. diameter and the driving wheels 6ft. 7½in., were also the same.

The locomotive was tried out for twelve months on the Scotch and Irish Mails ('Scotch' in this context is correct. On the London & North Western, a 'Scottish' express was one running wholly within Scotland) between Euston and Crewe. For some time it achieved a daily mileage of 310, being double-manned. From the reports, the running was very steady and although the trains worked were neither the heaviest, or fastest on the line, it gave every appearance of being a success. Webb claimed an average coal consumption of 26.6lbs. of coal per mile compared with 34.6lbs. for the four-coupled simple locomotives engaged on the same duties.

As a result of these tests, Webb decided that, in future, a high proportion of the North Western expresses would be worked by compounds. He, therefore, proceeded to build twenty-nine more locomotives similar to *Experiment*. This class, built in 1883-4, was known as the 'Compound' class, taking its name from the first of its members. *Experiment* had been found to be a little short of starting power and so the new class had the high-pressure cylinders increased to 13in. diameter. The low-pressure cylinder remained 26in., but had its steam ports increased to 16in. x 2in. The valve gear, again Joy, was modified to give a travel, in full gear, of 3⅛in. high-

A rare picture of a pair of three-cylinder compounds double heading. 'Experiment' No.1113 *Hecate* and 'Teutonic' No.1304 *Jeannie Deans* on Whitmore troughs.

3

pressure and 4½in. low-pressure, a return crank was driven off the rear big end; the lap was ¾in. and 1in. respectively. Independent control of the cut-off for high-pressure and low-pressure valve gear was provided and the pressure in the low-pressure valve chest limited to 75p.s.i. by means of a relief valve. The driver was provided with a valve by which to admit live steam direct to the low-pressure cylinder. Webb stated that this was to be used to warm up the cylinder, but drivers often tried to use it as an aid to starting, of which more anon.

The high-pressure steam chests were placed beneath the cylinders and the valves were of the 'Trick' type. The Joy valve gear to these had the motion discs carrying the quadrant bars fastened to the underside of the slide bars. The quadrant bars were each grooved to a radius equal to the length of the valve rod link. Working in the grooves were brass slide blocks, carried by the lifting links, to the lower end of which were attached the valve rod link and to the upper end, a compensating link on the connecting rod. A rod to the return crank on the high-pressure crank pin controlled the upper end of the compensating link. The reversing shaft was placed outside the trailing wheels and attached to the quadrant bars, which were extended below the discs for that purpose. The return crank was dispensed with in the last few of the class.

The low-pressure steam chest was on top of the cylinder and was fixed by two steel plates between the main frames.

These locomotives, thirty in number, following the rebuilding of *Experiment* to conform with the others, weighed 37¾ tons, of which 14 tons were carried on the leading, low-pressure driving wheels and 13¼ tons on the trailing, high-pressure ones. Despite the complications of compounding and the higher weight, some four tons, the 'Compounds' were unable to do the work of the two-cylinder simple 'Precedents'.

To cope with this and the increasing weight of trains, the 'Dreadnought' class was introduced in 1884. The first of the class was delivered only one month after the last five 'Compounds'. The new class, which eventually totalled 40 units, represented a complete reversal of the Crewe policy, instituted by Ramsbottom, of cheap, simple motive power. As well as a general and large increase in all dimensions, there were also some important mechanical differences from the 'Compounds'. The chief of these was the valve gear, on which Webb took out a patent. The cylinders, 14in. diameter high-pressure and 30in. low-pressure, had a stroke of 24in. Joy valve gear was once again used and the valve details were as follows: low-pressure, travel in full gear 4½in., lap 1in., lead ³/₁₆in.; high-pressure, travel in full gear 3½in., lap ⅞in., and lead ⅛in. The cut off for high-pressure and low-pressure gear could be varied independently.

Although the high-pressure steam pipes remained 3in. in diameter, the low-pressure pipes, or receivers, which were crossed in the smokebox as before, were enlarged to 5in. in diameter. The low-pressure relief valve was set to 80p.s.i.

A 'Dreadnought' class compound No.2058 *Medusa*.

Once again, the leading axle was carried in a radial axle box, but the crank axle, instead of being forged, was pressed and bent hydraulically. The boiler was much larger, having a total heating surface of 1,362sq.ft., pressed to 175p.s.i. These changes resulted in the weight in working order going up to 42½ tons, of which 15 tons were carried on each driving axle.

The second batch of twenty 'Dreadnoughts' had, as a result of earlier experience, a modified starting arrangement. The starting valve used on the 'Compound' and early 'Dreadnought' locomotives admitted live steam to the low-pressure valve chest. As a result, the low-pressure receiver became choked and the back pressure on the high-pressure pistons negated much of their work. To overcome this problem, the later system introduced a by-pass valve, under the control of the driver, which led the high-pressure exhaust directly into the blast pipe. It is, perhaps, significant that these engines took no part in the 1888 race to Edinburgh.

The ten 'Teutonics' of 1889-90 were built as a 7ft. 1in. driving wheel version of the 'Dreadnought' class. Ahrons has a fascinating story on how this came about. In the 1850s, the L&NWR had two locomotive superintendents and, in charge of Wolverton and the southern division, was J. E. McConnell. He designed a class of 2-2-2, inside framed express locomotives, which worked the best expresses on the southern division until about 1880. These were being scrapped at Crewe and the driving wheel centres were used on the 'Teutonics'.

These were, in the event, by far the most successful of the Webb compounds and, apart from the larger driving wheels, the most significant change was to the low-pressure valve gear. The inside Joy motion and reversing gear was removed; a loose eccentric, operating the valve rod through rocking levers, being put in its place. The eccentric was driven by stops in the left-hand crank webb and the low-pressure valve was, as a result, always in full gear. Reversing was automatic. When the engine was moved half a revolution, the low-pressure gear took up the correct direction of travel. The by-pass valve as used on the 'Dreadnought' class was, in this case, essential to prevent any steam from entering the low-pressure receiver before the valve was in the correct position to admit to the proper side of the low-pressure piston. At least four 'Experiments' and all the 'Dreadnoughts' were modified in this way.

Unfortunately, the valve was in the smokebox, which exposed it to a constant stream of hot ash and corrosive gases, which could only erode and cause the valve to stick. It has been recounted many times that Mr. Webb, not, as we have noted, a man renowned for a sense of humour, was less than amused to be asked, apparently in all innocence, to explain the resulting phenomena. What happed was as follows: Down would steam into Crewe Station, a majestic black locomotive, which then backed onto the London express, then coupled-up and which then stood hissing in that expectant manner peculiar to steam power. On being given the 'right-away', the driver would open the by-pass valve, select the high-pressure reverser to full forward gear and open the regulator. Two things then went wrong!

Firstly, the by-pass valve would stick and secondly the-uncoupled high-pressure driving wheels would begin to slip. This, of course, admitted the high-pressure exhaust into the low-pressure receiver and, as the low-pressure slip eccentric had not moved its requisite half revolution forwards, the low-pressure valve was still in the reverse position from the coupling-up procedure. At this point, to the amazement of the onlookers, and if the stories are true, to the fury of Mr. Webb, the low-pressure driving wheels would also begin to slip, but of course, in the opposite direction. The result was lots of steam, spinning wheels, noise and no doubt, swearing on the footplate, but as for forward or, indeed any motion of the train? No Sir!

Notwithstanding these gyrations, the loose eccentric made the gear so much more simple that all the succeeding classes of three-cylinder compounds were so fitted. There were other minor changes to the valve gear which contributed to the success of these locomotives. The valve travel was increased, by ¼in. in the case of the high-pressure and by a whole inch for the low-pressure. In place of the low-pressure exhaust clearance, there was now a small amount of exhaust lap to provide a cushioning effect to the large low- pressure piston. This helped to obviate the to-and-fro surging motion that had been so apparent in the earlier classes. The 'Teutonics' weighed 45½ tons in working order, of which 14½ tons was carried on the leading wheels and 15½ tons on each driving axle. They were by far the best of the three-cylinder Webb compounds and, the efforts of *Hardwicke* on the night of 22/23 August 1895 notwithstanding, probably as good as any other contemporary locomotive. Three examples will suffice. On the same night, No.1309 *Adriatic* brought the racing train from Boston to Crewe, 158.1 miles in 148 minutes, a record that stood for over forty years. On the first day of September, the North Western ran a train non-stop from Euston to Carlisle. The locomotive was the 'Teutonic' No.1306 *Ionic*, the crew, the same two who had control of *Hardwicke* eight days earlier. This was no speed record attempt; firstly the coal capacity of the tender and secondly, the stamina of the fireman precluded this, but the time of 353 minutes for the 290 miles remained the British record, until Gresley's corridor tenders made the London-Edinburgh non-stop possible in 1928. Thirdly, the star turn of the North Western for over eight-and-a-half years was the performance of No.1304 *Jeanie Deans* on the 2pm. Down express. It is unfortunate that Webb seemingly failed to appreciate how close to total success the 'Teutonics' were. In 1891, he produced a further enlargement of the compound express locomotive, the ten 'Greater Britain' class. The 'Teutonics' had proved to be a little short of starting power and so, in the new locomotives, the high-pressure cylinders were enlarged to 15in. diameter. The boiler represented an entirely new concept. It was very long and divided into two sections. The rear section, with tubes 5ft. 10in. long and 2^{1}/$_{8}$in. diameter, ended in a 2ft. 10in. combustion chamber. There was then a further section of tubes, 10ft. 1in. long, before the smokebox. The chamber had an ash hopper, with a weighted door actuated from the footplate. Whether any actual combustion took place in the chamber is doubtful and the front tube surfaces were of little value. The total heating surface was 1,466sq.ft. of which the firebox, this

'Greater Britain' class No.527 *Henry Bessemer*.

time without a water bottom, contributed 120sq.ft. As a result of the added length, an extra axle was fitted under the firebox, making the wheel arrangement 2-2-2-2, the leading axle had radial boxes, but the carrying axle had plain boxes with 1in. side play.

The valve gear was again changed completely, not, it must be said to the ultimate advantage of the locomotives. The Joy radial gear was abandoned and inside Stephenson's link motion used instead, with the eccentrics mounted on the trailing driving axle. The valve rods were very long and operated the top link of rocking levers, the lower ends of which carried the valve spindles. The first of the class had piston valves on the high-pressure cylinders, but these leaked and the subsequent members of the class had balanced slide valves working on vertical faces inside the frames. The low-pressure gear was again a simple loose eccentric on the leading driving axle. The weight in working order went up to 52 tons 2cwt., of which 31 tons were available for adhesion.

Webb, in common with Dougal Drummond on the South Western, built express engines with smaller driving wheels for the more steeply graded sections of the line. Thus, he followed the 7ft. 1in. 'Greater Britains', which were intended to work south of Crewe, with the 6ft. 3in. 'John Hick' class for the Crewe to Carlisle road. The original locomotive of the class was built in February 1894 and it was not until four years later that further examples were delivered. The second batch were fitted with piston valves, although their performance is shrouded with controversy. Most contemporary commentators have not one good word for them, but they ran from Carlisle to Crewe on some of the hardest turns for some time. Moreover, they were

'John Hick' class No.1548 *John Penn*.

the last of the three-cylinder compounds to survive the slaughter of the Whale era.

In 1897, Webb decided to cope with the ever-increasing weight of express trains by building another class of compound locomotives. This time the driving axles were coupled and four cylinders were used. The boiler was that of the 'Dreadnought' and 'Teutonic' classes, water bottom on the firebox and all and the first engine carried a pressure of 175p.s.i., but this was later raised to 200p.s.i.

In the three-cylinder compounds, the ratio between the volumes of the high-pressure and low-pressure cylinders was 1:2, very close to the generally accepted ideal ratio of 1:2.3, but on the four-cylinder locomotives, the cylinder sizes were 15in. diameter high-pressure and 19½in. low-pressure; the common stroke was 24in. This gave a ratio of 1:1.69 and the low-pressure cylinders were subsequently bored out to 20½in. Joy valve gear was used and one set drove the high-pressure and low-pressure valves on each side. The low-pressure valve spindle was extended out of the front of the steam chest and a horizontal rocking lever carried the motion to the outside valves. The high-pressure valves were pistons and balanced slide valves took care of the low-pressure distribution. There was no provision for varying the cut-offs independently.

The four cylinders were in line under the smokebox and the inside and outside cranks on each side set at 180 degrees, so eliminating the need for balancing weights for the reciprocating masses. The leading wheels were carried in a four-wheel radial truck. There were thirty-nine of these locomotives, the 'Black Prince' class, the fortieth, actually the second one built, being a 4-4-0 two-cylinder simple, built by the end of 1900.

'Black Prince' class No.1930 *Ramilles* as fitted with Belpaire firebox.

From 1901 till 1903, a further forty were built to a slightly enlarged design, the 'Alfred the Great' class. The boiler diameter went up from 4ft. 3in. to 4ft. 6¾in., resulting in a heating surface of 1,467sq.ft. and the high-pressure cylinders were increased to 16in. As the low- pressure cylinders were unchanged, down came the ratio again, this time to 1:1.64 and yet again changes had to be made. The high-pressure cylinders reverted to 15in. After Webb's retirement, his successor, George Whale, rebuilt the 'Alfreds' with an extra set of outside Joy valve gear. This allowed the high-pressure and low-pressure valves to be linked up independently when the driver wished. A single reversing screw was used which worked both reversing shafts.

By the grouping in 1923, most of the four-cylinder locomotives had been rebuilt as simples with two inside cylinders 18½in. diameter. However, nine 'Black Princes' and fifteen 'Alfreds' were still running as compounds. One of these, No.1974 *Howe*, had been superheated in 1921 and ran in this form until scrapped in 1928. Of the others, three 'Princes', Nos.1904, 1908 and 1923 and six 'Alfreds', Nos.1944, 1955, 1956, 1966, 1976 and 1979 were scrapped as compounds; the last of the rebuilds went to the scrap heap in 1931.

No.1941 *Alfred the Great* as running after conversion to 'Benbow' class.

The history of the Webb 0-8-0 freight locomotives is a complicated one, because over the years they were rebuilt, in most cases more than once. As on the North Eastern, the compound goods engines lasted longer than their passenger counterparts. Webb's first 0-8-0 No.2524 was, in fact, a two-cylinder simple, built in 1892. However, between 1893 and 1900, he built no less than one hundred and eleven three-cylinder compounds. The first, No.50, was delivered in 1893 and in this design he abandoned two of his treasured principles. One, of course, was forced on him in that the driving wheels had to be coupled, but surprisingly, he ceased to use divided drive and all the cylinders drove on the second axle. The three cylinders in line, were inclined at 1:8½ and had short 5ft. 8in. connecting rods. The cylinder dimensions were the same as the 'Greater Britain' class i.e. 15in. high-pressure, 30in. low-pressure and a stroke of 24in. The crank axle was built up from three separate pieces and also carried five eccentrics, four for the two sets of Stephenson link motion and the single loose eccentric for the inside valve. The bearings were very long and a centre bearing was also fitted. The high-pressure gear drove unbalanced slide valves on vertical faces, with the chests inside the frames; the low-pressure valve was on top of its cylinder, driven by the loose eccentric through a rocking lever.

The boiler was 13ft. 4in. between the tube plates and, unlike the passenger engines, had no combustion chamber. There were 210 tubes of 1^7/$_8$in. diameter giving a tube heating surface of 1,374sq.ft., the pressure was the usual 175p.s.i. and the grate area 20½ sq.ft. Boiler pressure was again 175p.s.i. The weight in working order was 49 tons 5cwt., all of which was, of course, available for adhesion. The driving wheels were 4ft. 5½in. diameter and the total wheelbase 17ft. 3in., the wheels being equally spaced.

The first of the 0-8-0s was tested between Stockport and Leeds using the dynamometer car. The gross load was made up to about 550 tons behind the tender, consisting of fifty loaded wagons and the car. Up the 1:135 gradient above Stalybridge, the speed was maintained at 23m.p.h and an indicated horsepower of 750 was recorded. The big engines took over heavy freight work on the main line

Three-cylinder class 'A' No.1801 at Carlisle in 1898.

Four-cylinder class 'B' compound, formerly No.1281, as LMS No. 8937.

over Shap and on the South Wales coal trains on the Shrewsbury and Hereford line.

Between 1901 and 1904, Webb built one hundred and seventy 4-cylinder compound 0-8-0s which turned out to be the most successful of the Webb compounds. They had the same cylinders as the 'Alfreds', i.e. 16in. x 24in. high-pressure and 20½in. x 24in. low-pressure. As in the three cylinder engines, all the cylinders drove the second axle and were steeply inclined. The driving wheels were again 4ft. 5½in. in diameter. The boiler pressure was 200p.s.i. and was the same as the 'Alfreds'. They were rostered to take loads of up to 900 tons on the main line and were the mainstay of the haulage of the 'Jellicoe Specials' during the First

Four-cylinder class 'E' compound, No.1222, when rebuilt as a 2-8-0.

World War, bringing coal from South Wales to the Grand Fleet at Scapa Flow.

These locomotives were extensively rebuilt. Thirty-eight were given a forward radial axle in an attempt to cure the 'nodding' action to which they were prone and of these twelve were fitted with a larger boiler having 1,753sq.ft. of heating area and the pressure reduced to 175p.s.i. In 1910, George Whale produced the first of the 'G' class 0-8-0 simples, in many ways similar to the original Webb 0-8-0 of 1892 and both he and Bowen-Cooke, who succeeded him at Crewe, rebuilt the Webb engines with the larger 'G' boiler. The three-cylinder machines were also rebuilt as two-cylinder simples at the same time and had all been so treated by 1912, although some of the rebuilds retained the smaller boiler for a time. Twelve of the four-cylinder locomotives received the large boilers as compounds, all 2-8-0s.

At the grouping, there were ninety-seven four-cylinder compounds in service. Fifty-nine small boiler 0-8-0s, twenty-six small boiler 2-8-0s and the twelve large boiler 2-8-0s remained. Of these, seventeen were withdrawn as compounds, the last in 1928 and the remainder converted to two-cylinder simples. Many were eventually fitted with superheated 'G2' or 'G2a' boilers and lasted well into the 1960s, but by 1928, the compound story was over.

Four-cylinder class 'F' compound 2-8-0 No.1273.

Webb's last compound design was for thirty 4-6-0 express goods engines. They were similar, mechanically, to the four-cylinder 0-8-0s, except that a four-wheel radial truck replaced the leading coupled axle, the high-pressure cylinders were reduced from 16in. to 15in. in diameter and the driving wheels were 5ft. 3in. in diameter. The inclined cylinders, all four in line, drove the leading coupled axle. They were intended for mixed traffic use and were known as 'Bill Baileys'. They were all scrapped by 1920, having been replaced by the simple class introduced by Whale in 1906.

There were also four three-cylinder compound tank engines built at Crewe between 1884 and 1887. The first was a rebuild of one of the familiar Beyer Peacock 'Metropolitan' class and so was a 4-4-0 with a leading bogie. The original boiler was retained, having a heating surface of 1,028sq.ft. and a pressure of 150p.s.i. The coupling rods were removed and the outside, high-pressure cylinders, 13in. diameter, were located below the foot-plating and the low-pressure 26in. The boiler pressure was 150p.s.i. and the total heating surface 1,028 square feet. Outside Joy valve gear drove slide valves below the cylinders. The bogie was replaced by a four-wheel radial truck and the condensing equipment was retained.

The 1885 locomotive was an attempt by Webb to produce a compound version of the standard 2-4-2 radial tank. It worked on the Broad Street and Mansion House service and, according to Ahrons, became the most unpopular locomotive with passengers ever built, as on the frequent starts, it imparted, at low speed, the surging, to-and-fro motion peculiar to all the small-wheeled Webb compounds. I can remember a similar feeling when riding in the first coach behind the two-cylinder Great Western tanks in the West Country, but by all accounts, this one could throw you off the seat! E. L. Ahrons, with the turn of phrase at which he was a master, said "Had the London and North Western Railway tank engines had names like the tender engines, I would have respectfully suggested the name 'Fore and Aft'; on one occasion when leaving Victoria (Underground) a full carriage of passengers were swinging backwards and forwards after the manner of a University Eight". The high-pressure cylinders were 14in. diameter and Ahrons states that the stroke was 18in. If this is true, it is difficult to imagine the designers' reasoning, although it would have the effect of giving a cylinder volume ratio of 1:2.3, better than any other Webb compound. Outside Joy valve gear was used again, but in this case, the valves were on top of the cylinders. The low-pressure cylinder with the more usual 24in. stroke had a diameter of 26in. The boiler had a total heating surface of 994sq.ft. and carried a pressure of 160p.s.i. The locomotive weighed 51 tons in working order.

The third engine, of 1887, was similar. However, to improve the starting power, the high-pressure cylinders were given the longer stroke of 20in. and, to try to appease the passengers by smoothing out the ride, the driving wheels were increased from 4ft. 8in. to 5ft. 9in.

The last of the compound tanks was described as a goods engine and the wheel arrangement was 2-2-4-0. The coupled axles at the rear were driven by the outside, high- pressure cylinders and the single, front driving axle by the inside low-pressure one. The leading wheels had the usual radial axle. The boiler was larger than the preceding tank compounds, having a heating surface of 1,099sq.ft. Although the freight was not expected to complain, the driving wheels were 5ft. 2in. in diameter. It would appear that this locomotive was no more successful than the others, as it did very little work on goods trains and was soon relegated to work the Manchester to Buxton slow passenger trains. When the boilers of these four locomotives fell in between 1897 and 1900, Webb scrapped them and built no more compound tank engines.

One more Webb compounding experiment must be noted. The second of the 'Teutonics' No.1302 *Oceanic* was built as a 'continuous expansion' locomotive. As the three cylinders, with the usual 24in. stroke, were 14in., 14in. and 20in. in diameter, 'continuous expansion' could not have meant 'triple expansion'. The cylinder dimensions suggest a three-cylinder simple, but it was soon converted to conform with the rest of the 'Teutonics' and Ahrons comments, "its doings as a continuous expansion engine were shrouded under an impenetrable silence". However, in 1895, Webb took the first experimental compound, the old 2-2-2 *Medusa* and again rebuilt it. Renamed Triplex, it became a three-cylinder triple expansion engine. Retaining the stroke of 20in., the three-cylinder diameters became 9¼in., 13in. and 19½in. The high-pressure cylinder was on the right, the intermediate on the left and the low-pressure inside. For starting, provision was made to admit high-pressure steam into the intermediate cylinder, Stephenson link motion actuated the outside valves and the inside valve gear was a loose eccentric, similar to that on the three-cylinder compounds. A new boiler was fitted, with a long smokebox to accommodate the receiver pipes; pressure was 200p.s.i. Ahrons says that this strange hybrid had difficulty starting, even with only one coach behind, although Webb himself used it occasionally to haul his inspection saloon. It was finally scrapped in 1903.

The work of the Webb compounds on the road varied between acceptable and downright disastrous, as erratic as their design was unique. For a long time, whenever a compound required a pilot, the North Western rules insisted that this must be a simple locomotive. The old 'Lady of the Lake' Class lasted into the twentieth century in this very role. Ahrons goes into some detail on the performance of the three-cylinder locomotives and was quite enthusiastic over the work of the 'Teutonics'. Reference has already been made to the surging motion which they imparted to the train and this was the first feature of which the passengers would be aware. Ahrons takes great pains to explain this phenomenon and produces graphs to illustrate the relative effects of various crank positions.

However, they did achieve mileage figures comparable with other express locomotives of this era and at times brilliant performances were recorded. Furthermore, there were other and not so innovative classes of locomotives on other railways at the same time, which were notably less successful. It is against the background of their own contemporaries and not by later standards that the Webb compounds must be judged. When new, the 'Compound' class worked turn and turn about with the famous 'Precedents' and Webb claimed that, on express working, in particular between Crewe and Euston, they burned 26.6lbs. of coal per mile, as against the 34.6lbs. needed by the 'Precedents', the boilers of both classes being precisely the same. Such claims, of course, mean little unless more details are given of train weights, average speeds and so on and in any case, this ignores the extra 10p.s.i. carried by the 'Compound' boilers. Anyway, it was soon found that they were not powerful enough and they were relegated to secondary duties, mostly working from Crewe to Manchester and Holyhead and on local duties on the main line. On these duties, they burned about 32lbs. of coal per mile. Two of the class were shedded at Rugby where the work was heavier, but the inability of the engines to run at any speed over about 60m.p.h, even downhill, meant that time was lost and the coal consumption was as high as 37.6lbs. per mile. This represents a firing rate of over 100lbs. of coal persq.ft. of grate area per hour and it is difficult to believe that much more than three quarters of the coal could be burned. The bill to the L&NW for lineside fires must have risen considerably at this time. The 'Precedents' in the same link worked these trains with much less fuss and as it has been proved, they were very free running engines. It would seem that the steam cycle of the 'Compounds' became choked and it may be that the drivers had trouble mastering the added complications of the independent cut-offs.

The 'Dreadnought' class, as well as being much more powerful, was also more consistent, although Ahrons describes their performance as 'streaky'. The loads were still light, about 155 tons being the average, but an early example of the potential of these locomotives was provided in March 1885 when No.504 *Thunderer*, ran from Liverpool to Crewe in 45 minutes - 43m.p.h - hauling a train of 228 tons. The train would almost certainly have consisted of six-wheeled stock and it must always be born in mind that the resistance of these would be almost twice that of modern coaching stock. Earlier in the same month, *Dreadnought* herself had worked the Down 'Scotch' express through from Euston to Carlisle at a running average speed of 44.7m.p.h. The train was quite light, about 130 tons, but even so, the coal consumption of 29.2lbs. per train mile represents 63lbs. persq.ft. of grate area per hour and the locomotive is stated to have steamed freely throughout. As the drivers and shed staff got the measure of the 'Dreadnoughts', the performances became more consistent. Runs quoted by Ahrons to demonstrate this include one by No.643 *Raven*, timed by Rous-Marten, when 190 tons was taken from Willesdon to Rugby, 77 miles in 85 minutes and Ahrons claims a net time of 77 minutes from Rugby to Crewe, including the very high maximum speed for a 'Dreadnought' of 72m.p.h down Whitmore Bank. Further north, No.511 *Achilles*, is credited with taking 160 tons from Preston to Carlisle in 100 minutes, an average speed of 54m.p.h, but these were the best of all the runs recorded. The official coal consumption of the whole class was given by the North Western as 37.7lbs. per mile.

The 'Teutonics' were easily the best and fastest of the Webb compounds. The star of the class was undoubtedly No.1304 *Jeanie Deans*, which worked the 2p.m. Down express from Euston to Crewe and the return Up working for over eight and a half years, from 1891 till 1899. The train was a heavy one, for the period and loads were generally between 250 and 300 tons. This remarkable performance, year in, year out, is probably unique and goes a long way towards disproving the premise that all the Webb compounds were failures. The running was steady rather than spectacular; the average speeds scheduled were 50m.p.h Down and 52m.p.h Up. On a typical run, Jeanie Deans took a load of 256 tons from Willesden to Rugby, 77¼ miles, in 91½ minutes. Although the downhill speed nowhere exceeded 61m.p.h, the uphill work was excellent, with a minimum of 42m.p.h on the climb to Tring.

The Webb compounds were certainly not among the success stories of British locomotive design and the mechanical theory was, to say the least, suspect. The large unbalanced forces produced by the uncoupled engines getting in and out of phase made them uncomfortable to ride on and behind and produced unnecessary mechanical stresses. The haste with which they were scrapped, or converted to simple propulsion has often been emphasised, but this was no quicker than on the North Eastern and a parallel could be drawn with the scrapping of steam locomotives in the 1960s in favour of dubiously better diesels, for no better reason than that it was 'fashionable'.

Details of the Webb compounds

Date	Type	H.P. Cyls	L.P. Cyls	Stroke	Class	No. Built	Driving Wheels	Weight T:cwt
1878	2-2-2	(1)9in.	(1)15in.	20in.	1	1	6ft. 0in.	23:5
1882	2-2-2	11.5in.	26in.	24in.	2	1	6ft. 6in.	37:15
1883	2-2-2	13in.	26in.	24in.	3	29	6ft. 6in.	37:15
1884	4-2-2-0	13in.	26in.	24in.	4	1	5ft. 9in.	46:17
1884	2-2-2-0	14in.	30in.	24in.	5	40	6ft. 3in.	42:10
1885	2-2-2-2	14in.	26in.	18in./24in.	6	1	4ft. 8½in.	50:17
1887	2-2-4-0	14in.	30in.	24in.	7	1	5ft. 2½in.	55:00
1887	2-2-2-0	14in.	26in.	20in./24in.	8	1	5ft. 8½in.	52:00
1889	2-2-2-0	14in.	30in.	24in.	9	10	7ft. 1in.	46:10
1891	2-2-2-2	15in.	30in.	24in.	10	10	7ft. 1in.	52:02
1893	0-8-0	15in.	30in.	24in.	11	111	4ft. 5½in.	49:05
1894	2-2-2-2	15in.	30in.	24in.	12	10	6ft. 3in.	52:00
1897	4-4-0	15in.	(2)19½in.	24in.	13	1	7ft. 1in.	53:18
1899	4-4-0	15in.	(2)20½in.	24in.	14	38	7ft. 1in.	54:08
1900	4-4-0	16in.	(2)20½in.	24in.	15	40	7ft. 1in.	57:12
1901	0-8-0	15in.	(2)20½in.	24in.	16	170	4ft. 5½in.	53:10
1903	4-6-0	15in.	(2)20½in.	24in.	17	30	5ft. 0in.	60:00

No.54 *Medusa*
Built at Crewe 1846
Rebuilt as two-cylinder compound 1879
Rebuilt as Triplex 1895   Withdrawn 1903

No.66 *Experiment*
Built Crewe 1882

'Experiment' class
300-520 Built Crewe 1883   311-372 Built Crewe 1884

300 *Compound*	315 *Alaska*	1102 *Cyclops*
302 *Velocipide*	321 *Servia*	1104 *Sunbeam*
303 *Hydra*	333 *Germanic*	1113 *Hecate*
305 *Trentham*	323 *Britanic*	1111 *Messenger*
306 *Knowsley*	353 *Oregon*	1115 *Snake*
307 *Victor*	363 *Aurania*	1116 *Friar*
519 *Shooting Star*	365 *America*	1117 *Penguin*
520 *Express*	366 *City of Chicago*	373 *Emperor*
311 *Richard Francis Roberts*	310 *Sarmation*	372 *Empress*
	1120 *Apollo*	

'Dreadnought' class
503 & 508 Built Crewe 1884   504- 2064 Built Crewe 1885
2-1395 Built Crewe 1886   637- 648 Built Crewe 1888

503 *Dreadnought*	2058 *Medusa*	1370 *City of Glasgow*
504 *Thunderer*	2059 *Greyhound*	1379 *Stork*
507 *Marchioness of Stafford*	2060 *Vandal*	1395 *Archimedes*
508 *Titan*	2061 *Harpy*	637 *City of New York*
509 *Ajax*	2062 *Herald*	638 *City of Paris*
510 *Leviathan*	2063 *Huskisson*	639 *City of London*
511 *Achilles*	2064 *Autocrat*	640 *City of Dublin*
513 *Mamoth*	2 *City of Carlisle*	641 *City of Litchfield*
515 *Niagra*	173 *City of Manchester*	643 *Raven*
685 *Himalaya*	410 *City of Liverpool*	644 *Vesuvius*
2055 *Dunrobin*	437 *City of Chester*	645 *Alchymist*
2056 *Argus*	545 *Tamerlane*	647 *Ambassador*
2057 *Euphrates*	659 *Rowland Hill*	648 *Swiftsure*
	1353 *City of Edinburgh*	

'Teutonic' class
1301-1303 Built Crewe 1889   1305-1312 Built Crewe 1890

1301 *Teutonic*	1304 *Jeanie Deans*	1309 *Adriatic*
1302 *Oceanic*	1305 *Doric*	1311 *Celtic*
1303 *Pacific*	1306 *Ionic*	1312 *Gaelic*
	1307 *Coptic*	

'Greater Britain' class
2053 Built Crewe 1891   2054 Built Crewe 1893
2051- 772 Built Crewe 1894

2051 *George Findley*	2054 *Queen Empress*	528 *Richard Moon*
2052 *Prince George*	525 *Princess May*	767 *William Cawkwell*
2053 *Greater Britain*	526 *Scottish Chief*	772 *Richard Trevithick*
	527 *Henry Bessemer*	

'John Hick' class
20 Built. Crewe 1894   1505-1559 Built Crewe 1898

20 *John Hick*	1534 *William Froude*	1549 *John Rennie*
1505 *Richard Arkwright*	1535 *Henry Maudsley*	1557 *Thomas Savary*
1512 *Henry Cort*	1536 *Hugh Myddleton*	1559 *William Siemens*
	1548 *John Penn*	

'Black Prince' class
Built 1897-1900

*	1901	*Jubilee*	(5156)	*	1921 *John of Gaunt*	(5134)
*	1902	*Black Prince*	(5157)	*	1922 *Intrepid*	(5146)
$	1903	*Iron Duke*	(5110)	@	1923 *Agamemnon*	(5115)
@	1904	*Rob Roy*	(5111)	*	1924 *Powerful*	(5183)
*	1905	*Black Diamond*	(5137)	*	1925 *Warrior*	(5147)
*	1906	*Robin Hood*	(5149)	*	1026 *La France*	(5180)
*	1907	*Black Watch*	(5178)	*	1927 *Goliath*	(5116)
@	1908	*Royal George*		*	1928 *Glatton*	(5173)
*	1909	*Crusader*	(5159)	*	1929 *Polyphemus*	(5117)
*	1910	*Cavelier*	(5172)	*	1930 *Ramillies*	(5142)
*	1911	*Centurian*	(5112)	*	1931 *Agincourt*	(5136)
*	1912	*Collosus*	(5113)	*	1932 *Anson*	(5161)
*	1913	*Canopus*	(5132)	*	1933 *Barfleur*	(5169)
*	1915	*Implacable*	(5114)	*	1934 *Blenheim*	(5165)
*	1916	*Irresistable*	(5155)	*	1935 *Collingwood*	(5133)
*	1917	*Inflexible*	(5184)	*	1936 *Royal Sovereign*	(5150)
*	1918	*Renown*	(5131)	*	1937 *Superb*	(5154)
*	1919	*Resolution*	(5160)	*	1938 *Sultan*	(5161)
*	1920	*Flying Fox*	(5166)	*	1939 *Temeraire*	(5158)
*	1257	*Invincible*	(5144)	*	1940 *Trafalgar*	(5144)

LMS numbers in brackets.
1901 Built as four-cylinder simple.
* Rebuilt as 'Renown' class two-cylinder simple.
@ Scrapped as compound, 1908 in1923.
1904 & 1923 did not carry their allotted LMS numbers.

'Alfred the Great' class four-cylinder 4-4-0
Built 1901-1903

*	1941 *Alfred the Great*	(5179)	*	1952 *Benbow*	(5119)
*	1942 *King Edward VII*	(5185)	*	1953 *Formidable*	(5120)
*	1943 *Queen Alexandra*	(5145)	*	1954 *Galatea*	(5121)
@	1944 *Victoria & Albert*	(5118)	@	1955 *Hannibal*	(5122)
*	1945 *Magnificent*	(5139)	@	1956 *Illustrious*	
*	1946 *Diadem*	(5138)	*	1957 *Orion*	(5148)
*	1947 *Zillah*	(5174)	*	1958 *Royal Oak*	(5181)
*	1948 *Camperdown*	(5141)	*	1959 *Revenge*	(5143)
*	1949 *King Arthur*	(5152)	*	1960 *Francis Stevenson*	(5153)
*	1950 *Victorious*	(5186)	*	1961 *Albemarle*	(5140)
*	1951 *Bacchante*	(5136)	*	1962 *Aurora*	(5171)

'Alfred the Great' class *(continued)*

* 1963 *Boadicea*	(5163)	* 1972 *Hindostan*	(5168)
* 1964 *Caesar*	(5123)	* 1973 *Hood*	(5175)
* 1965 *Charles H. Mason*	(5151)	@ 1974 *Howe*	(5128)
@ 1966 *Commonwealth*	(5124)	* 1975 *Jupiter*	(5167)
* 1967 *Cressy*	(5125)	@ 1976 *Lady Godiva*	
* 1968 *Cumberland*	(5164)	* 1977 *Mars*	(5129)
* 1969 *Dominion*	(5126)	* 1978 *Merlin*	(5177)
* 1970 *Good Hope*	(5127)	@ 1979 *Nelson*	(5130)
* 1971 *Euryalus*	(5135)	* 1980 *Neptune*	(5182)

LMS numbers in brackets.
* Rebuilt as 'Renown' class two-cylinder simple.
@ Scrapped as compound 1928. Superheated in 1921.
None of the un-rebuilt locomotives carried their LMS numbers.

Three-cylinder compound 0-8-0
Built 1893-1899
All rebuilt as two-cylinder simples 1904-1909

a. Class 'C' (Originally Class A) Rebuilt 1904-1906 with large boiler.
b. Class 'C1' Rebuilt 1909 retaining small boiler.
c. Class 'D' Rebuilt 1906-1909 with large boiler.
LMS number in brackets.

1801 (8977) b	1819 (9058) c	1837 (9055) c	1856 (9026) c
1802 (9016) c	1820 (9050) c	1838 (9032) c	1857 (9042) b
1803 (8967) a	1821 (9064) c	1839 (9010) c	1858 (8996) b
1804 (9017) c	1822 (9005) c	1840 (8975) b	1859 (8994) b
1805 (8959) a	1823 (8965) a	1842 (8966) a	1860 (8956) a
1806 (8984) b	1824 (9035) c	1843 (9048) c	1861 (8972) b
1807 (8961) a	1825 (9053) c	1844 (8985) b	1862 (8968) b
1808 (9047) c	1826 (8995) b	1845 (9003) c	1863 (9006) c
1809 (8971) b	1827 (9018) c	1846 (9059) c	1864 (9063) c
1810 (8955) a	1828 (8957) a	1847 (8982) b	1865 (9062) c
1811 (8991) b	1829 (8988) b	1848 (9022) c	1866 (9002) c
1812 (9014) c	1830 (9014) c	1849 (8987) b	1867 (8973) b
1813 (9060) c	1831 (9039) c	1850 (8970) b	1868 (9056) c
1814 (8960) a	1832 (9038) c	1851 (8992) b	1869 (8988) b
1815 (9044) c	1833 (9009) c	1852 (8993) b	1870 (9057) c
1816 (9045) c	1834 (9028) c	1853 (9036) c	1871 (9030) c
1817 (8999) b	1835 (9001) b	1854 (9023) c	1872 (9015) c
1818 (9013) c	1836 (9061) c	1855 (8964) b	1873 (9007) c

Three-cylinder compound 0-8-0 *(continued)*

1874 (9054) c	2530 (9049) c	2539 (9031) c	2548 (9004) c
1875 (8974)b	2531 (8978) b	2540 (9020) c	2549 (8953) a
2524 (9011) c	2532 (9029) c	2541 (8953) a	2550 (8976) b
2525 (9008) c	2533 (8979) b	2542 (8990) b	2551 (9034) c
2526 (9043) c	2534 (9000) c	2543 (8981) b	2552 (9052) c
2527 (9051) c	2535 (8986) b	2544 (9040) c	2553 (8958) a
2528 (9027) c	2536 (9033) c	2545 (8980) b	2554 (8997) b
2529 (8954) a	2537 (9019) c	2546 (8969) b	2555 (8998) b
	2538 (8962) a	2547 (9012) c	

Most re-built with G2A boilers and some again with Belpaire fireboxes.

Four-cylinder compound 0-8-0
Built 1901-1905

a. Class 'B'. Withdrawn as built.
b. Class 'E'. Rebuilt 1904-1908 as 2-8-0.
c. Class 'F'. Rebuilt 1906-1908 as 2-8-0 with 'Experiment' boiler.
d. Rebuilt as 0-8-0 simple.
LMS number in brackets.

18 (9602) b	842 (9338) d	1047 (9387) d	1227 (9363) b
41 (9362) d	843 (8906) d	1051 (8922) d	1228 (9142) d
134 a	859 (9336) d	1055 (9377) d	1229 (9070) d
352 (9611) c	898 (9146) d	1061 (8923) a	1230 (9387) d
405 (8907) d	899 (9610) c	1064 (9607) b	1231 (9147) d
410 (9331) d	904 (9337) b	1065 (9340) b	1233 (8928) a
437 (9374) b	906 (9612) c	1066 (9272) d	1236 (9351) b
500 (9265) d	916 (9354) d	1070 (9120) d	1237 (8929) d
503 (9068) d	918 (8948) d	1088 (8924) d	1240 (9358) d
508 (9090) d	1017 (9605) b	1091 (8925) d	1241 (9346) d
509 (9069) d	1035 (9133) b	1094 (9324) d	1242 (9388) d
640 (9383) d	1036 (9365) c	1110 (9369) d	1243 (9150) d
641 (9151) d	1038 (9349) b	1122 (9099) d	1245 (9073) d
644 (8950) d	1039 (8918) d	1190 (9076) d	1247 (9613) c
647 (9615) b	1040 (8920) d	1222 (9608) b	1248 (8930) d
813 (8903) d	1041 (9355) d	1223 (9368) b	1249 (8931) d
815 (9375) d	1042 (9606) b	1224 (9350) d	1271 (9145) d
823 (8904) d	1043 (9304) d	1225 (8926) d	1272 (8932) d
826 (8905) d	1044 (9376) d	1226 (8927) d	1273 (9614) c

Four-cylinder compound 0-8-0 *(continued)*

1274 (9071) d	1401 (9075) d	1893 (9085) d	2369 (8910) d
1276 (9389) d	1404 (8933) d	1894 (9361) d	2387 (9357) d
1277 (9149) d	1432 (9384) d	1895 (9066) d	2496 (8911) d
1278 (9381) d	1436 (8951) d	1896 (9380) d	2556 (8912) d
1279 (9352) d	1448 (9373) d	1897 (9370) d	2557 (8913) d
1280 (9100) d	1449 (9122) d	1898 (9385) d	2558 (9603) b
1281 (8937) a	1543 (8952) d	1899 (9382) d	2559 (8914) d
1282 (8938) a	1547 (8946) a	1900 (9065) d	2560 (8915) d
1283 (8939) d	1555 (8949) a	2024 (8934) d	2561 (8916) a
1284 (8941) d	1585 (9609) b	2036 (9341) d	2562 (9152) d
1285 (9339) d	1586 (9353) b	2038 (9356) d	2563 (9604) b
1286 (9347) d	1881 (8900) a	2056 (9359) b	2564 (8917) d
1287 (8942) d	1882 (9344) d	2057 (9371) d	2565 (8919) a
1288 (8943) d	1883 (9319) b	2060 (9392) d	2566 (9153) d
1289 (9361) d	1884 (9266) b	2074 (8908) d	2567 (8921) d
1299 (9074) d	1885 (9267) b	2080 (8940) d	2568 (9342) d
1300 (9379) d	1886 (9390) b	2114 (9386) c	2569 (9072) d
1308 (8944) d	1887 (9148) d	2118 (9392) d	2570 (9367) c
1310 (8945) d	1888 (9600) b	2163 (9393) c	2571 (8935) d
1318 (9366) d	1889 (9345) b	2208 (9364) d	2572 (8936) d
1353 (9335) d	1890 (8901) d	2251 (9067) d	2573 (9373) c
1369 (9372) c	1891 (9348) d	2271 (9360) d	2574 (9343) c
1370 (8947) a	1892 (8902) d	2342 (8909) d	2575 (9394) d
			8818 (9132) d

Most again re-built with G2A boilers and some again with Belpaire fireboxes.

Chapter 2

Great Eastern Railway

The two-cylinder compound system, designed by Mallet, was improved upon by Schinau and Von Berries in Germany and by T. W. Wordsell in England. The development of expansive valve gears, notably the Williams-Howe link motion, which was adopted as their own by Robert Stephenson & Co., led, after 1842, to greater economies in working. Wordsell looked upon compounding as a further means of improving the thermal efficiency, without sacrificing the basic two-cylinder layout with its inherent simplicity. He hoped to do this by forcing the drivers to work the engine so as to use the expansive properties of steam. In an article in *The Engineer* in 1885, he put it thus: "As made, a locomotive can take steam for about 90% of the stroke, by increasing the lap and altering the lead of the valves it would be possible to reduce the maximum admission to 50%. If, however, this were to be done, there would be four positions of the driving wheels at which no steam could get into the cylinders and the engine could not be moved, either backwards or forwards. With an admission of a little over 50%, while one cylinder could not take steam to go ahead at all, the other might be so near the end of the cylinder that that a locomotive with a heavy train could not start   The compound system gets over the whole difficulty at once". Well, hope springs eternal! This was only half the story. In fact, with a compound locomotive, starting was a major problem and each designer attempted to solve the difficulty with his own system of valves to admit high-pressure steam to low-pressure cylinders. In 1882, Wordsell built, at Stratford, a series of twenty two-cylinder simple 2-4-0s with 7ft. driving wheels and 18in. x 24in. cylinders. The 1884 compounds were based on this design, with one cylinder, the right hand one, enlarged to 26in. diameter. The slide valves, driven by Joy radial valve gear, were above the cylinders. To carry the additional weight, a leading bogie was fitted in place of the single leading axle of the simples. The boiler had a total heating surface of 1,200sq.ft., of which 117sq.ft. was contributed by the firebox. The total weight in working order was 44 tons, of which almost 30 tons was available for adhesion. The valve settings were the same for each cylinder with a travel, in full gear, of 5in., a lap of $1^{1}/8$in. and a lead of $^{3}/16$in.

As originally built, the starting arrangement was a simple valve to admit live steam to the low-pressure cylinder and, with the light trains of the day, it was only necessary to use this if the high-pressure piston happened to stop at top dead centre. However, this was inconvenient, clumsy and sometimes troublesome to use, as the steam passed round the intermediate receiver the wrong way and choked the

T. W. Wordsell's Great Eastern Railway compound 4-4-0 No.230.

high-pressure cylinder. Ahrons has quoted the designer as stating that this resulted in a failure to start about once in ten attempts, This was enough to make the drivers prefer to back the engine, in order to get the high-pressure piston in the best position for starting, a time-consuming operation which could take three or four minutes. To solve this problem, a second valve, this time a flap or 'intercepting' valve was fitted in the receiver pipe. It was closed from the footplate before the starting valve was opened and automatically opened by the first exhaust blast from the high-pressure cylinder. This was the basis of what became known as the Wordsell- Borries compound system.

There were eleven of the compounds and it would seem that the boiler steamed well in spite of the blast pipe being 80% larger than that fitted to the simples. This seems to have reduced the tendency, inherent in two-cylinder compound engines, because of the fewer, but fiercer blasts, to pull the fire to pieces, Indeed, a Great Eastern driver, singing the praises of the compounds, is quoted as calling the blast "as soft as silk". The boiler pressure was at first 160p.s.i. and James Holden, who succeeded Wordsell at Stratford, carried out some tests which showed a 14% fuel saving when compared with the simples. However, when the boiler pressure was reduced to 150p.s.i., the advantage fell to 2%. It must be said that the simples, Class G14, have been described by O. S. Nock as "awfull sluggards". The compounds were powerful engines, which performed well at low speeds, but when called upon for faster running, choked up the steam cycle. The low-pressure cylinder was too small and this, combined with the fact that the valve gear was set for equal events in high-pressure and low-pressure cylinders, resulted in a strangled steam circuit,

Holden built one further two-cylinder compound locomotive after Wordsell's departure, in 1887. This was a modification of one of the 4ft. 10in. 0-6-0 goods engines and may have been influenced by the success of the North Eastern 'C' class of the previous year. The cylinders were again 18in. and 26in. in diameter with a common stroke of 24in. Stephenson link motion was fitted and the slide valves were again arranged for equal events in the high-pressure and low-pressure sides, so it is not surprising that it was no more successful than the earlier locomotives.

Chapter 3
Great Western Railway

In 1886, William Dean built two tandem compound 2-4-0 locomotives as an experiment. Ahrons reports that Dean felt that he had a duty to try compounding and on a different system from that used on other British Railways. The first of his locomotives, No.7, was a standard gauge, outside framed 2-4-0, which, except for the distance of 10ft. 2in. between the front truck and the driving wheels, looked entirely conventional. The 'works' were, however, anything but! The four cylinders, all inside, were arranged in tandem, with the low-pressure pair in front and the high-pressure pair in line and behind. The diameters were 23in. and 15in. There was a single piston rod on each side, which after passing through the low-pressure gland, was guided by a bronze bush held centrally in a hollow casing and bolted to the rear of the low-pressure cylinder fitting into the bore of the high-pressure. Each pair of cylinders was formed of one casting and located with centres 2ft. 3in. apart. The piston rod itself was 4in. in diameter at the

Above: William Dean's standard gauge compound 2-4-0 No.7 of 1886.

Right: The similar, but unsuccessful, Dean broad gauge compound 2-4-0, No.8.

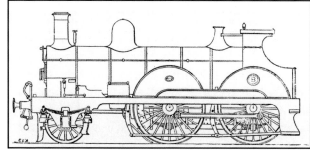

low-pressure end and tapered to 3½in. in the high-pressure cylinders. The common stroke was 21in. Balanced slide valves, actuated by Stephenson's link motion, were used below the high-pressure cylinders and on vertical faces alongside the low-pressure. The valve spindles were connected to the top and bottom of a crescent-shaped yoke, to the centre of which was attached the main valve rod. The valve settings were rather peculiar. They were set to give equal port openings at each end of the stroke with very little lead. As a result, there was a great deal of compression at each exhaust point. The driving wheels were 7ft. diameter and the leading truck, which had side play in the boxes, had 4ft. diameter wheels. A form of starting valve, to admit live steam to the low-pressure cylinders, was fitted to assist in starting.

The broad gauge engine, No.8, shared the same boiler and frames, with the addition of an extra pair to carry the outside bearings to the leading wheels and the footplate; the driving wheels thus had four inside bearings. As with all broad gauge locomotives at this time, except the renewed 8ft. singles, this was done with a view to eventual conversion. The boiler was pressed to 180p.s.i. and had a total heating surface of 1,258sq.ft. The cylinder arrangement was completely different.

The cylinders themselves were again cast in two parts, with 2ft. 3in. centres, but in this case, the low-pressure pair were to the fore and the piston rods were forked and passed down each side of the high-pressure cylinders. The high-pressure crosshead, which was carried in two slide bars, had lugs projecting from each side, to which the low-pressure piston rods were connected. The cylinders were inclined at an angle of 1:12 and all the steam chests were below. Direct drive Stephenson's link motion was used to activate the valves. The cylinders had a common stroke of 21in. and diameters of 14in. high-pressure and 22in. low-pressure.

The standard gauge locomotive ran for some time on slow passenger trains between Swindon and Cardiff. The main problem was the lack of lubrication to the bush on the piston rod between the low-pressure and high-pressure cylinders. The rod siezed on a number of occasions. The broad gauge engine was an almost total disaster. Only one recorded instance of its use in service exists. It was called on to assist a heavy train up the gradient through Box Tunnel and, in the resulting chaos, broke three piston rods, three pistons and blew the covers from all four cylinders. Although relief valves were provided on the low-pressure valve chests, trapped water broke the cylinder covers on at least two other occasions. The very small clearance volume, a common fault on early compounds, contributed to this problem. No more compounds ran on the Great Western for nearly twenty years.

During the first ten years of the present century, the most advanced locomotive development in Britain took place under the supervision of G. J. Churchward at Swindon. He set as his target, a locomotive capable of exerting a pull of two tons at the drawbar, at a speed of 70 miles per hour. There was almost certainly no railway in Britain in 1900 which possessed such a machine. Churchward's enquiring mind looked further afield than most of his contemporaries and, as his paper to the Institute of Civil Engineers in 1903, 'American Locomotive Practice', shows, he was attracted by the simple, robust American construction methods. He was even more impressed by the finesse of the European school and in particular by the performance of the de Glehn compound 'Atlantics' on the Chemin de Fer du Nord. By this time, he had three of his own new locomotives, Nos.100, 98 and 171 in service. These were 4-6-0s with two outside cylinders and were built in 1902-3. Churchward took the unprecedented step of persuading the Great Western Board of Directors to sanction the purchase in 1903, of one of the French locomotives and to follow it with two more larger ones in 1904 to find out, by the most direct means, whether the de Glehn locomotive had the advantage over a simple engine of his own design.

In view of the importance of the design features of these locomotives and their subsequent effect on British locomotive practice, it is worth digressing from the strict subject matter of this work to consider the history of this memorable design. Its origins go back, strangely enough, to a Swindon trained engineer. Thomas Russell Crampton was Chief Draughtsman for the Great Western, who left in 1844 to set up his own engineering firm in London. He attempted to produce a standard gauge locomotive, which would be comparable to the Gooch 8ft. singles then running on the 7ft. gauge. He decided that stability required a low centre of gravity, a premise which only McConnell at Wolverton had, up to this time, been brave enough to dispute; to combine this with a large steam capacity. Crampton pitched a big boiler very low and, to avoid such fancy devices as axles through the middle of boilers, put the driving wheels behind the firebox. The cylinders were brought back to the centre of the locomotive and, with no pitching moment, the 'Cramptons' were very smooth riding. They were fitted with outside link motion and the cylinders were located between the double frames to maintain rigidity.

Altogether, thirty-four 'Cramptons' were built for British railways, but none of them were very successful. On the Continent of Europe, it was a different story. The first French 'Cramptons' were built for the Nord in 1849 and of the 137 built for various railways, some were still at work into the twentieth century. In Germany, fourteen railways bought 135 of them. Crampton had the assistance of French engineers in the detailed design work and the proportions of the resulting locomotives were excellent. They were as large as Gooch's 8ft. singles and the link motion gave a better steam distribution, but most of all, the steam circuit was very free. The large steam passages and ports which he used were never bettered and, indeed, not until Chapelon began his work of rebuilding the French 'Pacifics', even equalled.

In 1885, Alfred de Glehn, Chief Engineer of the Society Alsacienne de Construction Mecaniquies and Gaston du Bousquet, Chief Rolling Stock Engineer of the Nord, began their long and fruitful collaboration. Taking the Crampton principles of chassis and steam circuit design and adding their own ideas on

The original de Glehn compound, No.7 of 1885, displayed in the Cité du Train at Mulhouse.

compounding, they built No.701, a four-cylinder compound 2-2-2-0. The driving wheels were uncoupled, as in the Webb compounds and the high- and low-pressure cylinders drove different axles. As rebuilt with a leading bogie in 1892, today this historic locomotive has pride of place in the Cité du Train (City of the Train) at 2, rue Alfred de Glehn, 68200 Mulhouse, France. In 1891, they built two further locomotives for the Nord, again one of these was a 4-2-2-0, but in the other, the driving axles were coupled. As the uncoupled wheels proved no advantage in running, all subsequent examples had coupled driving wheels. The outside, high-pressure cylinders were in the Crampton position, just behind the bogie, and drove the second coupled axle, while the low-pressure cylinders were underneath the smokebox and drove the leading axle. There were independent valve gears for each pair of cylinders, each with its own cut-off adjustment and the de Glehn system of by-pass valves to allow simple operation when exceptional power output was required.

Unlike the general situation in Britain, there was, at the time, close co-operation between the major French railways and, as a result, locomotives of the same type were ordered for and ran on, the Midi, Est and Oest as well as the Nord. The Paris-Orleans followed suit in 1899. Du Bousquet was, however, unhappy with the steam circuit and, as a result of his experiments, the 'Atlantics' of 1900 had the steam pipes considerably enlarged. By 1905, similar locomotives were operating most of the crack expresses in France. The sort of work which these engines achieved in normal day-to-day running can be found in the 1902 summer timetable of the Nord. The star turn was undoubtedly the Paris to Arras run of 120 miles in 117 minutes, but in addition, there were no less than 16 runs scheduled at over 55m.p.h. Rous-Marten recorded instances of them maintaining the French legal speed limit of 77$\frac{1}{2}$m.p.h. with loads of up to 300 tons on level track.

Here was just the sort of performance Churchward was looking for on the Great

Western and at a meeting of the Society of Locomotive Engineers in November 1902, he announced that he had placed an order in France for one of the compound 'Atlantics'. Whether Churchward intended to build compounds to his own designs is doubtful, as long as he could achieve the same economy of working and power output from a simple, but his experiments had not by 1903, arrived at this point. Even if comparable expansion ratios could be achieved, the losses through condensation in one cylinder would, in theory, be considerably more than if the expansion were spread over two. This is because the difference between the inlet and exhaust temperatures is less in a compound engine and the drying of steam by effective superheating was still in the future. Furthermore, the four-cylinder compounds were complex machines to handle and, it must be said, the standard of education of drivers in France was considerably higher than that to be found on this side of the Channel.

La France was built for the Great Western by the Society Alsacienne des Construction Mechaniques at Belfort and delivered to Swindon in thirteen packing cases in October 1903, where she was erected. As delivered, the engine was a copy of the Nord 'Atlantics' except for the draw-gear, which was adapted to take a standard Great Western tender, brakes, smokebox door and chimney. She entered service in February 1904 and proved equal to any demands that the normal Great Western expresses could make including the inaugural Paddington to Plymouth non-stop. Rous-Marten travelled on the first service from Paddington to Swindon, but said that neither the speed nor the load made any demands on the capacity of the locomotive: on a later run he timed a speed of 84.9m.p.h on level track.

The French boiler was constructed in three sections, the smoke-box forming a fourth, the rear section having a diameter of 4ft. 9⁵/₁₆in. and the forward, 5ft. The lagging, however, was flush and gave the impression of a parallel boiler. 126, 2³/₄in. 'Servre' tubes were fitted, giving a nominal tube heating surface of 2,288sq.ft. This figure is a little misleading as these tubes were of a corrugated section, giving a theoretical increase in surface area, but were of doubtful value in actual steam production. The barrel was 13ft. 7¹/₂in. long and was pitched with the centreline

de Glehn compound 'Atlantic' No.102 *La France* in original condition as delivered and with the livery of 1903.

8ft. 3¼in. above rail level. The narrow firebox had a grate area of 29½sq.ft. and contributed 167sq.ft. of heating surface.

The four cylinders had common stroke of 25³/₁₆in. and diameters of 13³/₈in. for the outside, high-pressure and 22¹/₁₆in. for the inside, low-pressure pair. They were located in the standard de Glehn positions. Four sets of Walschaerts valve gear were fitted and the high-pressure valves were balanced slide valves in the 'modern' position above the cylinders, although they were buried in the footplating. The ordinary flat valves for the low-pressure cylinders were above the cylinders and offset at an angle of 40 degrees. The cut-off could be varied independently or, at the driver's will, in any fixed ratio. There was also provision for working as a simple by means of a transfer valve, which directed the high-pressure exhaust up the chimney and, at the same time, fed live steam to the low-pressure cylinders via a reducing valve. This is visible in early photographs of No.102 high up on the right-hand side of the smoke-box.

The only changes made in the life of the locomotive were in the boiler. In 1909, the original boiler was re-tubed with plain tubes in place of the 'Servre'. By this time, Churchward was proceeding apace with the fitting of superheaters and in September 1913, No.102 was dealt with. At this stage, the original boiler was again retained and, fitted with top feed and new outside steam pipes, had a two-row

de Glehn compound No.103 *President* at Paddington carrying the GWR standard taper boiler.

superheater installed. The boiler now had 139, 2in. tubes, 12 5¹/8in. flues and 96, ⁷/8in. superheater elements, which with a firebox area of 168sq.ft. gave a total heating surface of 1,706sq.ft. This arrangement lasted for about three years. The weight had, so far, been pretty much as built, i.e. 64 tons 13cwt., of which 33 tons 7cwt. rested on the driving axles; the tender weighed a further 43 tons.

In September 1916, a standard Swindon boiler was fitted, similar to that carried by the 'Stars' and 'Saints'. This had 176, 2in. tubes, 14, 5¹/8in. flues and 84 superheater elements which, with 155sq.ft. of fire-box area, gave a total heating surface of 2,171sq.ft., the boiler centre line was raised and a shorter safety valve cover was fitted to keep within the loading gauge. The Swindon boiler was heavier and the total weight went up to 68 tons 9cwt. and the adhesion weight to 34 tons 15cwt. New outside steam pipes, of the same pattern which became so familiar on the 'Castles' and 'Kings' in later years, were fitted. The number and name plates were on the cab side sheets, with the coat-of-arms and maker's plates on the leading and trailing driving wheel splashers. As first put into service, the livery was in lined-out black, but this was changed to standard Great Western green in October 1905.

La France was tested against the Churchward two-cylinder simple 'Atlantics', fourteen of which were built in 1904-5. To provide a comparison with the four-cylinder simple locomotive which he was building, Churchward sought from the Great Western Board, permission to buy two of the larger French compound 'Atlantics' which were then, in 1905, working on the Paris-Orleans Railway. They were again built at Belfort and were taken into Great Western stock in June 1905, having first had the same modifications as No.102 to make them suitable for British conditions. The boiler was an enlarged version, again built in three rings, but with the middle one overlapping. The 'Servre' tubes gave a nominal heating surface of 2,577sq.ft. The cylinders were also larger, 14³/8in. high-pressure and 23⁵/8in. low-pressure, which with 6ft. 8in. diameter driving wheels gave a nominal tractive effort of 27,174lbs. They were numbered 103 and 104 and ran without names until 1907 when, to celebrate the signing of the 'Entente Cordiale', they were named *President* and *Alliance*.

The boilers of these locomotives went through the same rebuilding as that of No.102, with the exception that, in order to provide a spare, No.104 was fitted with standard taper boiler in 1907, while the 'Servre' tubes in the original boilers were replaced. No.103 also got a taper boiler in 1910, but by 1912, they were again carrying the French ones, by this time fitted with superheaters, but not in the original order. That is, No.103 had boiler number 104 and No.104 that of 103. They were both finally fitted with the same standard No.1 taper boiler as *La France*, in fact No.103 received hers in January 1914 and No.104 in July 1915. Thus the oldest of the French boilers, lasted the longest.

As these locomotives were purchased to compare their performance with the

Churchward four-cylinder simples, the first of these, No.40, afterwards *North Star*, was built as an 'Atlantic'. The tests carried out on the Great Western between 1904 and 1909 convinced Churchward that compounding was an unnecessary complication. Alfred de Glehn recommended, for high-speed work, that his locomotives be worked at cut-offs of 55% high-pressure and 65% low-pressure. At these settings, *La France* met the famous target of 2 tons pull at the drawbar at 70m.p.h. The question to be asked in the tests was whether or not Churchward could produce a simple locomotive which could also do this? In order to be comparable, it had to be obtained at, or about, the equivalent ratio of expansion, that is about 20% cut-off. The cut-off figure is, in itself, meaningless if the valve ports are so restricted as to preclude a good charge of steam entering the cylinder at each stroke and conventional valve setting methods of 1904 did not allow this to happen at such short cut-offs. Churchward was not the first British locomotive engineer to appreciate that long-travel, long-lap valve gear was the solution, but many considered that the increased valve speeds associated with the increase in travel would add to the wear and lubrication problems to an unacceptable degree. Even such a distinguished an engineer as Nigel Gresley stuck to this view as late as 1923, to the detriment of his early 'Pacifics'. The truth is that, although in full gear the travel is longer, this will only be at low speeds and when the engine is linked up, it will, at a cut-off of 20%, have no more valve travel than that of a short lap engine working at, say 35% and with better port openings to boot.

It is a great pity that so little official information exists on the tests run to compare these locomotives with Churchward's own product. None of the dynamometer test rolls have survived and very few logs of runs exist in which the engines were extended in any way. Perhaps, the best effort recorded by No.102 was on the Birmingham line in 1913 by Cecil J. Allen. *La France* had charge of the Up mid-day, two hour, express. The load out of Birmingham was 10 coaches, 300 tons, of which one was slipped at Warwick and three detached at Leamington. This left a load of 185 tons for the last 87 miles. North of Leamington, there were three severe permanent way restrictions and a minute and a half was dropped on the 25 minute schedule for the 23 miles. After the Leamington stop, the locomotive was opened up to some purpose and after some impressive uphill work, the fine stretch down the bank from Beaconsfield to Park Royal was taken at an average speed of 75m.p.h., with a maximum of 86½ at Denham. There were slight signal checks in from Park Royal, but even so, the time of 86½ minutes for the 87 miles from Leaminqton is quite impressive.

Rous-Marten timed No.104 on the 'Cornish Riviera' in 1905, at that time still via Bristol. It is a pity that the details are rather typical of his work and incomplete. On the Down run, a load of 230 tons was taken non-stop to Plymouth in exactly the scheduled time of 267 minutes, but this includes a dead stop at Laira and Exeter was passed just over four minutes early. On the Up train, with a load of 235 tons,

Churchward's four-cylinder simple No.40, built as an 'Atlantic' in 1906 for comparison with the de Glehn compounds, was rebuilt as a 4-6-0 and eventually named *North Star*.

a steady run resulted in a five minute gain on schedule, all west of Exeter. Good steady, economical running with on time arrivals is all that the railway authorities could ask and the French compounds appear to have given that. Why then did Churchward not adopt compounding in his standard locomotives?

There is no record of the transfer and reducing valves giving any trouble and the mechanical complication of four sets of valve gear is not much more than two sets between the frames with rocking levers. The Great Western drivers had no trouble mastering the skill of linking up the independent cut-offs to get the best from the engines. No, Churchward found that his own four-cylinder simples were much more free running, especially when working hard. All else being equal, the steam cycle of the compound must, by its nature, be more tortuous. Of course, we now know that the 'Stars' were by far the best design of British express locomotive to take the road before the First World War and it was probably only against them that the compound 'Atlantics' would come off second best and a close second at that. Only the four-cylinder simples were worked with comparable expansion ratios to the compounds: right till the end of steam, the two-cylinder locomotives were always worked with longer cut-offs and part regulator opening.

What then, was the legacy of the French design in Britain? It is true to say, almost everything about it, with the sole exception of the compounding, was adopted by the Great Western. Divided drive, bogie design and, as Churchward described it, the "watch makers" motion, all became standard. Perhaps, the most remarkable part of all was the story of the big-end. The design was adopted as standard on the Great Western, taken to the LMS by Stanier and to Doncaster in 1949 by K. J. Cook, to cure once and for all the Achilles heel of the Gresley 'Pacifics'. Finally, the same design was used in the ill-fated *Duke of Gloucester*, the last British express passenger steam locomotive.

The French compounds, after their displacement from top-link duties, worked secondary expresses in the Oxford and Birmingham areas until their withdrawal in the mid-twenties. The last to go was No.104 in September 1928.

Details of the Great Western compounds

Four-cylinder 2-4-0 tandem compound No.7.
Built Swindon 1885. Withdrawn 1887.

Four-cylinder 2-4-0 tandem compound 7ft. gauge No.8.
Built Swindon 1885. Withdrawn 1886.

Four-cylinder 4-4-2 No.103 *La France.*
Built Belfort, delivered October 1903.
Rebuilt with superheater 1913.
Rebuilt with Swindon No.1 boiler 1916.
Withdrawn October 1926.

Four-cylinder 4-4-2 Nos.103 *President* and 104 *Alliance.*
Built Belfort, delivered 1905.
Rebuilt with Swindon No.1 boiler 1909-1915.
Withdrawn No.103 March 1927, No.104 September 1928.

Chapter 4
North Eastern Railway

T. W. Wordsell was appointed Locomotive Superintendent of the North Eastern Railway in 1885, having occupied that post on the Great Eastern since 1881. The failings of his compounds on that line are described in another chapter, but those he designed at Gateshead were much more successful. The locomotive affairs of the North Eastern were in a turmoil at the time of his arrival, as a result of the precipitate departure of his predecessor, Alexander McDonnell. The design work had been in the hands of a committee, under the chairmanship of the General Manager, Harry Tenant and included two engineers whom we will meet again - W. M. Smith and Wordsell's younger brother, Wilson. The result of their handiwork can be seen today in the little 2-4-0 in the National Railway Museum at York. The elder Wordsell soon had matters in hand. Prior to his service on the Great Eastern, he had enjoyed a varied career. He had spent some time at Altoona, described as the Crewe of the U.S.A. and had returned to Crewe itself as Works Manager under Webb. Here, he was involved in the early compounding experiments.

In view of the nature of most of the traffic on the North Eastern, it is not surprising that the first of the Wordsell compounds was an express goods locomotive. No.16 was the first 0-6-0 compound to work in this country. As was to be expected, this was a two-cylinder locomotive, utilising the Wordsell-Von Borries system. Completed in the Autumn of 1886, it was the prototype for the 'C' class, which eventually totalled 171 units. The cylinders were of the same dimensions as the Great Eastern locomotives, that is 18in. high-pressure and 26in. low-pressure diameters, with a stroke in both of 24in. Steam distribution was by Joy valve gear and the slide valves had a travel, in full gear, of 5½in., with a lap and lead of 1⅛in. and 3/16in. respectively. The ratio of cylinder volumes was on the low side at 1:1.44, but the difference from all previous two-cylinder compounds and probably the secret of their success, was the fact that the valve gear was set up to give a longer cut-off in the low-pressure side than that of the high-pressure. This, of course, effectively increased the cylinder ratio and prevented choking of the receiver. The actual arrangement was such that, with a high-pressure cut-off of 73%, full forward gear, the low-pressure figure was 86%; a typical running setting of 50% high-pressure gave 73% in the low-pressure cylinder.

The total weight in working order was 41 tons 16cwt. The boiler, which became a North Eastern standard, had a total heating surface of 1,136sq.ft., a pressure of 160p.s.i. and a grate area of 17.2sq.ft. It was on these engines that Wordsell introduced his crank axle with circular cheeks. In contrast with the then normal built-up type, it was robust and could be easily machined on a lathe. It was an example of a thoroughly practical design, from a man with a machine shop background.

A large enclosed cab with side windows was fitted, lined with wood and seems to have been well received by the footplate crews. Some years earlier, two locomotives had been built for the Stockton and Darlington section of the North Eastern with similar cabs, but such had been the protests from the men at being 'shut in', or (may one suggest such a thing?) being considered 'soft' by less fortunate colleagues, that subsequent engines reverted to a simple weather-board. In his book 'Locomotives of the North Eastern Railway', O. S. Nock recalls a visit to the small shed at Penrith in the 1930s and describes the contrast between the cab of a 'C', by then, of course, rebuilt as a simple and what he calls "the stark ironmongery" of a North Western 'Cauliflower' parked alongside.

Class 'C' 0-6-0 No.874. Built 1889.

The compounds were put on the longer hauls which the main line goods link undertook from Newcastle to York and Leeds and across the country on the South Durham and Lancashire line. They also did a considerable amount of passenger work, especially after their displacement from the top goods links. In 1887, the *The Engineer* was so enthusiastic as to say, "Even if no saving of fuel is effected, the North Eastern Railway Company has obtained a splendid engine which does infinite credit to the builder as well as the designer!". The designer claimed that considerable savings in fuel were effected, as compared with what he described as "ordinary" engines in the same link, but as these were older and less powerful, perhaps the comparison is not quite fair. Ten similar, simple, locomotives were built with two 18in. x 24in. cylinders and on the mainline turns burned 40.9 tons of coal per mile against the 34.9 tons in the case of the compounds. This difference was contributed to by the lower boiler pressure, 140p.s.i., carried by the simple engines.

The second class of compound locomotives on the North Eastern was a 0-6-2 tank, the cylinders, motion and boiler of which were identical to the 'C' class 0-6-0s. They were designed for the shorter hauls from the Northumberland and Durham pits to the sea and fifty one were built. The lack of the additional brake power provided by the tender when working loose-coupled mineral trains did not make these locomotives popular with the crews, moreover, the valve gear arrangement made them somewhat unhandy, as when in reverse, the difference in the cut-off was in the wrong sense; the low-pressure valve cut-off some 20% before the high-pressure. As the loads were always much much heavier in one direction than the other, the disadvantage was less marked in traffic. Nevertheless, probably for this reason, Wordsell never built a compound passenger tank engine.

Class 'B' 0-6-2T No.1152.

Following the success of his freight locomotives, Wordsell introduced the first of his North Eastern compound express classes, the 'D'; unlike his Great Eastern compounds, a 2-4-0. This was possibly in deference to the McDonnell fiasco, part of which had centred around the swing link bogies on the 4-4-0s. The first 'D', No.1324, had the same cylinder and valve arrangements as the 'B' and 'C' classes, except that the valve travels were marginally shorter. The boiler, however, was much larger and was fitted with brass tubes giving a total heating surface of 1,323sq.ft. The grate area was 17.33sq.ft. Why the second 'D', No.340, was built as a 2-4-0 is something of a mystery, as by the time it was delivered, twenty 4-4-0s were on the road. No.340 appeared in December 1888 and was distinguishable from No.1324 by the extended frames and running plate at the front end. These

Class 'D' 2-4-0 No.1324. Built 1886 at Gateshead.

covered the long tail rods from the piston valves, which were fitted to both high-pressure and low-pressure cylinders. These were W. M. Smith's patent valves with 2in. spring-loaded relief valves fitted to each end of the cylinders to allow any trapped water to escape. This prevented a hydraulic lock, which would blow the ends from the cylinders and were unnecessary with slide valves, which would lift off their seats to achieve the same end. There were three valves, one 7in. diameter for the high-pressure cylinder and two 5½in. diameter for the low-pressure. These were above the cylinder, side by side and actuated by a forked rod.

With a boiler pressure of 175p.s.i. and 6ft. 8in. driving wheels, these were by far the most powerful express locomotives the North Eastern had had up till that time and were fast and free runners. However, the absence of a bogie and the fact that at speed, unequal amounts of work were being done in the two cylinders, made for unsteady running. Both locomotives were rebuilt as 4-4-0, two-cylinder simples in 1896 and with the later addition of a superheated boiler, lasted into the 1930s, No. 1324 being withdrawn in 1930 and No.340 in 1933.

The 'D' class could be described as a prototype for the next class, the 'F' class

Class 'D' 2-4-0 No.340. Built 1888. Fitted with Smith Piston Valves.

4-4-0s. The first of these, Nos.18, 42 and 115 appeared from Gateshead Works in June 1887 and a total of twenty 4-4-0s were built by the end of that year. They had the single splasher over the coupled wheels and the large two side window cab, which was used on all subsequent North Eastern locomotives. These cabs were not as roomy inside as their outside appearance would indicate. The boiler, with its mountings, projected about 2ft. into the cab space and the aft end of the splasher, with a wooden seat on top, ran down the full length on each side. The floor was so low that footboxes were fitted alongside these to enable the enginemen to see out of the front spectacles. This left the fireman a space of about 2ft. wide in which to ply his trade. Ten of the locomotives were simples and the other ten compounds, similar to the 'D' class, No.1324, except for the provision of the leading bogie. Fifteen more compounds, Nos.1532 to 1546, were built at Gateshead in 1890 and 1891 after Wilson Wordsell had succeeded his brother. Neither the bogie nor the large side window cab seems to have caused the Geordie enginemen any problems whatsoever. A further development was made to the starting system which, the reader will recall, had, on the Great Eastern locomotives, utilised two levers, one operating the starting and the other an intercepting valve. This was now simplified to one lever only. A small, spring-loaded lever was operated by the driver, which opened the starting valve, admitting live steam to the low-pressure cylinder and at the same time putting steam onto a single acting piston, which closed the intercepting valve in the low-pressure receiver. As soon as the engine moved, the lever was released and the first exhaust blast from the high-pressure cylinder blew the intercepting valve open.

The main reason for the easy acceptance of these locomotives, with their previously controversial features, was their mastery of the tasks that they were set. The McDonnell '38' class were no advance, on the road, over the Fletcher '901s' they were supposed to replace, whereas the 'Fs' were an advance in all senses over the 'Tennants'. In the 1888 Race to Edinburgh, they were used north of Newcastle and on the night of 31st August, Driver Nicholson took 100 tons behind No.117 to Edinburgh in about 130 minutes for the 124 miles. The 'F' Class worked the major East Coast expresses for six years before being displaced by the later 'M' Class. The close working relationship which existed between W. M. Smith and S. W. Johnson, the Midland Railway Locomotive Superintendent, led to a considerable exchange of technical data at this time between Derby and Gateshead. There was, for example, a good deal of work carried out on the Midland in the design of the Smith piston valves. In 1886, Smith's counterpart at Derby, Holt, had patented the steam sanding system, which resulted in the re-appearance on some British railways of the single driver express locomotive. Problems with the balancing and with tyre wear on four coupled high speed locomotives made some engineers look again at the simplicity of the single driver at this time. Furthermore, it would not have escaped the notice of the engineers at Gateshead that south of

York, both the 2-2-2 and 4-2-2 locomotives were putting up some impressive performances. As Ahrons wrote, "One could prove mathematically that they never could do it but there must have been some flaw in the premises, for they nearly always did". "It", was the Stirling singles of the Great Northern taking trains of up to 250 tons, through greasy-railed tunnels from King's Cross out to Potters Bar, unaided. The answer would seem to lie in the low frictional losses for a single, enabling a larger proportion of the indicated horsepower to be converted to drawbar horsepower. Experiments in Germany at a slightly later date, were to show that the coupling rods could account for up to 20% of the frictional resistance of a locomotive.

In 1888, new motive power was needed for the Leeds to Scarborough commuter trains and, given the light loads and an easy road, a single was the obvious choice. The ten class 'I' singles were built between 1888 and 1890 and had the same cylinders and motion as the 'F' class 4-4-0s. However, because of the larger driving wheel diameter of 7ft. 1in., the smaller standard boiler of the 'B' and 'C' classes was used, pitched with the centre line 7ft. 8in. above the rail level. There was no room for the valves between the cylinders, but as the usual Joy radial valve gear was used, placing them on top, with vertical faces, made for a simple, straightforward layout. As Dr. W. Tuplin has said, "about as simple as a compound locomotive could be".

Class 'I' 4-2-2 No.1530. Built 1890.

The second class of North Eastern compound singles was not only intended for main line work but, indeed, to replace the existing 4-4-0s on the crack expresses. The 'J' class consisting of ten units, was built in 1889-90 and with them Thomas Wordsell reached the end of his active career; in the process he produced a very fast and free running engine. The boiler was again the standard 4ft. 3in. diameter as on the 'I' class with the important difference that the grate area was increased to 20.7sq.ft. It supplied steam to the two 24in. stroke cylinders, the high-pressure being 20in. and the low-pressure 28in. in diameter. To get two such large cylinders between frames no more than 4ft. apart called for considerable ingenuity. They were set at 2ft. centres with the low-pressure higher than the high-pressure one and with its centre line sloping down towards the rear. Similarly, the lower high-pressure cylinder sloped upwards. Even so, the low-pressure cylinder wall projected

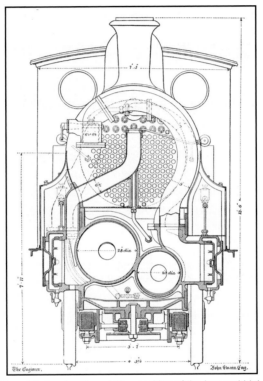

Cross section of a Class 'J' showing the relative position of the low and high-pressure cylinders.

through a hole in the right hand frame. As a result, there was no room between the frames for the valve chests and these were placed outside the frames, which were cut away to take them. This presented the designer with another problem; how to drive the valves? The solution was to be the Achilles heel of the 'J' class and it would seem that someone in the Gateshead drawing office had an off day in its conception. The Joy valve gear actuated the valves through a complicated system of rocking levers. This had no less than three horizontal and two vertical levers as well as a heavy crosshead. What is more, some of the joints were off-set. Dr. Tuplin again commented, "This layout was inexcusably bad - - - and nobody could really

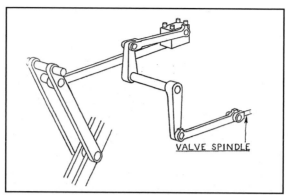

The complicated system of rocking levers for actuating the Joy valve gear on the NER 'J' class.

have trusted it". The result of this was a crop of broken valve spindles, cracked steam chests and what was most unusual, even broken valves.

The valve settings were the subject of some experiments, but the final result was a travel, in full gear, of 4³/₈in., a lap of 1¹/₈in. a lead of ³/₁₆in. in the high-pressure cylinder and a travel of 5³/₄in. in the low-pressure. As in the other Wordsell compound classes, the valves were arranged to give a later cut-off in the low-pressure side than in the high-pressure. The low-pressure receiver was a neatly fixed pipe around the inside curve of the smokebox.

The running of these engines in their original, compound, form, was the subject of some tests in 1889 with the first two, Nos.1517 and 1518. During the course of these trials, a speed of 90m.p.h. was claimed by No.1517 hauling a train of about 150 tons. In 'Locomotives of the North Eastern Railway', O. S. Nock accepts the figures of these tests. However, Dr.Tuplin in 'North Eastern Steam' casts doubts on the ability of the 'J' class to achieve the claimed power output. There was considerable correspondence in *The Engineer* in April and May 1890 on the subject. The official figures are presented in the following table:

Speed	Cut-Off H.P.	Cut-Off L.P.	I.H.P
5	63	78	136
17	63	78	438
23	50	68	498
30	50	68	630
50	43	62¹/₂	662
75	47	67	1041
86	53	79	1086

Dr. Tuplin considers that the higher speeds and power out-puts were over optimistic but, as O. S. Nock says, the cut-offs indicate that the engine was being

Class 'J' 4-2-2 No.1525 with outside steam chests.

worked very hard and whether the boiler could have sustained this sort of effort for very long, is certainly open to question. Dr. Tuplin's proposition is that, given the weight of the locomotive and train of 224 tons, 1,069 indicated horse power is not enough to produce a speed of 86 miles per hour on level track. There is no indication in the report of the location of the trial, or of the gradients involved.

The 'Js' weighed 46 tons 13cwt. in running order, of which 17¾ tons rested on the driving axle. They were T. W. Wordsell's last compound design as he retired in 1890, living in retirement in the Lake District until 1919. His influence in Britain on locomotive design was slight, but in Europe many hundreds of compound locomotives were built to his patents. The weakness in the valve gear of the big singles hastened their conversion to simple propulsion and by 1896, they had all been altered. The Achilles heel was removed and the rebuilds were given the new Smith piston valves, actuated by a simple, well-designed Stephenson link motion. They remained very fast and infinitely more reliable power units.

The new Locomotive Superintendent of the North Eastern was another Wordsell, this time the younger brother, Wilson. He had followed his brother to the United States and back to Crewe, but when T. W. went to Stratford, Wilson had come to Gateshead. Increasingly, the power behind the North Eastern locomotive throne became vested in W. M. Smith. He had a very varied career, including spending some time in Japan, but in 1883, he returned to England and Gateshead, for good. The third member of the locomotive hierarchy was Vincent Raven, Assistant Mechanical Engineer from 1895. Unlike his boss, Raven was an out-and-out North Eastern man. He had been an apprentice under Edward Fletcher and at the time of this appointment was 37 years old. This, then, was the new team and it wasted no time in making changes. Out went two cylinder compounds and Joy valve gear and in came link motion and piston valves.

There was one exception. In 1892, the first of the new express locomotives No.1620 of class 'M', was delivered from Gateshead. The new class was, externally

A rare view of No.1619, 'M' Class, at work as built. The location is Stannington and the train is made up of the first East Coast Joint Stock with dining car.

at least, an enlargement of the earlier 'F' class. It had the same large, side-windowed cab and the same single splasher covering both driving wheels, but apart from a general enlargement, there were other important differences. However, it is the third 'M', No.1619, which concerns us here. Delivered from Gateshead in May 1893, No.1619 was a two-cylinder compound version, with one low-pressure cylinder of 19in. diameter and one high-pressure of 28in. The common stroke was 26in. The boiler had a heating surface of 1,341sq.ft. and a grate area of 19½sq.ft. and carried a pressure of 200p.s.i., as against the 180p.s.i. of the simples. In common with these, the valve chests were outside the frames and the valves, actuated by a neat arrangement of link motion (the lesson of the 'J' class appears to have been absorbed by someone in the Gateshead drawing office), worked on vertical faces. They were driven by a single drop arm and rocking lever, through a hole in the frame and must have been greatly appreciated by the running shed staff.

Wilson Wordsell did not share his brother's enthusiasm for compounding and the Directors of the North Eastern, probably under his influence, commissioned a report in October 1893 'with reference to the working of Compound Engines compared with the working of other Classes of Engines on the North Eastern Railway'. The tests were carried out by Vincent Raven and produced some of the very few details of the work of this locomotive that have ever been published. On the road between Newcastle and Edinburgh, the compound returned the best coal consumption figures, but hardly good enough to produce a conclusive result. The cylinder arrangement was basically that of the 'J' class and the valve chests were placed higher than on the simples, to clear the low-pressure cylinder where it projected through the frames. This gave the locomotive a 'double breasted' look, similar to the Drummond 4-6-0s on the South Western. In the original form, No.1619 worked turn and turn about with the simples for five years and, as far as can be known, was as much a master of the tasks set as they were. However, in 1898, the engine was rebuilt at Gateshead, in a form which might well have become the prototype express engine for the future of the North Eastern and did, in fact, become so for the LMS twenty-five years later. This was W. M. Smith's patent three-cylinder compound in which the cylinder arrangement, of one inside high-pressure and two outside low-pressure cylinders allowed all three to be approximately the same size.

As first rebuilt, No.1619 had a high-pressure cylinder 19in. diameter by 26in. stroke and two low-pressure cylinders 20in. x 24in. The high-pressure valve was the latest development of Smith's piston valves, in which the rings were in the form of segments designed to collapse inwards to release any trapped water; the low-pressure cylinders had ordinary slide valves. The link motion was arranged so that the cut-offs to the high-pressure and low-pressure engines could be varied independently. The steam passages between the high-pressure exhaust and the low-pressure inlet were large enough to eliminate the need for the receiver pipe with which the two-cylinder compounds were provided.

A completely new boiler was fitted, having a total heating surface of 1,328sq.ft. and a grate area increased to 23sq.ft.; the pressure remained 200p.s.i.. Another Smith patent device, cross water tubes in the firebox, was fitted. At first, there was no means of access to these and so no way of cleaning, or replacing them. A new firebox with exterior covers to allow of their removal and repair without a major shopping was fitted in 1900.

The system of controls on this locomotive was, for a steam locomotive in the nineteenth-century, very complicated; although this was a deliberate design feature to take advantage of the possibilities of the compounding. It is interesting that,

Class 'M' No.1619 as rebuilt with 3 cylinders.

unlike the majority of locomotive designers before and since, Smith was an engineer and draughtsman and not a running department man. In producing this engine he concentrated on getting the steam through the cylinders with the least restriction and the engineering complication reflected this. The steam cycle of a compound engine is inevitably more circuitous than that of a simple and in many designs choking has occurred, either in the valve ports, or in the low-pressure receiver; No.1619 did not suffer from this. Starting, as ever, presented peculiar problems, which Smith overcame in as simple a way as possible. He arranged for the engine to start as a two-cylinder simple, admitting live steam to the two low-pressure cylinders only. When the driver felt that he had his train well on the move, he could operate a 'change valve', which altered the steam cycle, cutting off the live steam from the low-pressure valve chests and admitting it to the high-pressure one, thus starting compound working. In addition, there was another control at the driver's hand; this permitted him to increase the power output, for as long as the boiler would stand it, by feeding live steam into the low-pressure receiver while working compound. This was known as semi, or reinforced compound working. It was to prevent choking the receiver when working thus, that Smith provided No.1619 with independent cut-off to the high-pressure and low-pressure cylinders. The driver could, at the same time as he sent the live steam into the low-pressure cylinders, lengthen the cut-off to make the best use of the steam and to keep the back pressure on the high-pressure cylinder to a minimum.

No.1619 was a success and ran 21,000 miles on top link duties in the first four months. However, she was manned by selected and specially trained footplate men and the management of the locomotive department considered that the locomotive was too different for the average crew to handle. In addition to the controls, the fire grate was 20% larger than the 'M' class. Too long to go between the driving axles, it was long and shallow and required particular care to get the best results. The North Eastern was to get into trouble with the first 4-6-0 locomotives for the same reason only a few years later. Obviously, some time would be required before sufficient crews could competently handle a fleet of these locomotives and, as so often is the case, there was no time. Express engines of advanced power were urgently needed for the East Coast trains and instead of more compounds, Wordsell built a class of two-cylinder simples. Now, had the class 'R' been anything but totally superior to the current locomotives on the North Eastern, a case could have been made for more compounds, but No.2011 and the rest proved to be as good as any other contemporary 4-4-0 and better than most. So No.1619 remained unique and when her second, still saturated boiler wore out in 1930, it was not considered economic to build a single non-standard boiler. She was scrapped at Darlington in October 1930, having run 909,331 miles; latterly from Bridlington on the Hull, Scarborough and Leeds turns.

Wilson Wordsell was essentially a Victorian engineer, both in training and in his products. Like others of his contemporaries, he ran into trouble when he tried to increase the size of his locomotives beyond the confines of a standard 4-4-0 chassis. The 'S' and 'S1' 4-6-0s were unimpressive in performance and expensive to maintain and the first 'Atlantics', class 'V', were heavy on coal. These larger engines could out-perform an 'R' sometimes, but in service rarely did. It is said that W. M. Smith was ill when the design of the 'V' 'Atlantics' was being prepared and that on his return, he was less than pleased with some of the details. Be that as it may, the next two North Eastern 'Atlantics' which appeared in 1906, seemed to owe more to Derby than Gateshead and whether the Chief Mechanical Engineer had anything at all to do with their design must be open to doubt. Smith died later in the year and it would seem, the impetus went out of the development of the compounds, but even as built, they were the best locomotives on the railway.

The four cylinders were all in line under the smokebox and the arrangement was the same as Webb had used on the North Western, that is high-pressure outside and low-pressure inside. The stroke of both was 26in. and with diameters of 14¼in. and 22in., the volume ratio was 1.54:1. Piston valves, located above, were used in both sets of cylinders, 7¼in. for the high-pressure and 10in. for the low-pressure. Only two sets of valve gear were needed as, because the cranks on each side were diametrically opposed and inside admission used for the high-pressure and outside for the low-pressure, the valves moved in unison, the first locomotive, No. 730, had Stephenson's link motion, but the second, No.731, had a form of Walschaerts gear. The steam cycle was extremely free, as great care had been taken in the design of the exhaust passages.

The boiler was fitted with a Belpaire firebox, with cross water tubes and a distance of 14ft. 7¼in. between the tube plates. With 242 2in. tubes in the 5ft. diameter barrel, the total heating surface was 1,991sq.ft., a reduction of over 400sq.ft. as compared with the 'V' class. The smaller boiler was necessary in order to keep the

Class '4CC' No.731. 4-cylinder compound 'Atlantic' fitted with Walschaerts Valve Gear.

weight down, but in the event, there was no shortage of steam. To take advantage of the compound engine, the high boiler pressure of 225p.s.i. was carried. The Smith reducing valve was fitted, which permitted semi-compound working when an exceptional power output was required and the driver had independent control of the high- and low-pressure cut-off.

The two four-cylinder 'Atlantics' were for the year 1906, magnificent locomotives. They were capable, even before superheating, of power outputs in excess of 1,000 drawbar horse power and, on tests with the dynamometer car, proved able to sustain Churchward's famous target of '2 tons pull at 70 miles per hour'. In late 1906, the dynamometer car was used to test the capacities of the North Eastern express stud. The locomotives involved were: 'R' No.2028, 'S1' No.2114, 'V' No.784 and the compound No.730. The test runs took place between York and Newcastle and the trains were very heavy, even the 'R' was expected to take 350 tons. In the event, the compound swept the field. On the south bound run, she took 435 tare tons from Darlington to York in 45½ minutes; the maximum speed was 67m.p.h. and the average, start to stop, of just over 55m.p.h. As near to Darlington as Croft Spa, 2.6 miles, the speed had reached 55½m.p.h. and this was maintained up the gradient to Eryholme, producing a drawbar horsepower, corrected for gradient, of 1,030. The average speed from Danby Wiske to Benningbrough was 64.6m.p.h. and, except for the short rise between Thirsk and Sessay, this was achieved with the valve gear set for a cut-off of 53% high-pressure and 63% low-pressure, equivalent to about 33% in a simple. The boiler pressure was maintained at between 215 and 225p.s.i. for the whole run. Even better, was the running of No.730 on the northbound test train. The load was made up to not less than 456 tons tare and the timing was that of the 'Flying Scotsman' i.e. 97 minutes non-stop over the 80 miles from York to Newcastle. One of the features of the North Eastern running at that time was the extremely vigorous starts and this run was no exception. The first 5.5 miles to Benninbrough took only 8 mins. 2 seconds and, as might be expected, this brought the boiler pressure back to 190p.s.i., but by Alne, 11 miles from the start, the cut-off was notched up to 40% high-pressure, 54% low-pressure, and the pressure had recovered to over 200p.s.i. The speed was maintained at over 50m.p.h. through to Durham, an excellent performance with a train of this size. With the cut-offs at 47% high-pressure and 58% low-pressure, a maximum speed of 72m.p.h. was achieved at Chester-le-Street and over 70m.p.h. down the Team Valley to Bensham. The running time from York was 90 mins. 35 seconds. The 'S1' 4-6-0 on a run at the same time, but with a load lighter by 90 tons, made the good time of 94 minutes, but one example shows the superiority of the compound. Both trains passed Newton Hall Junction at 48m.p.h., but the speed of No.730 had been a full 10m.p.h. less, at 31m.p.h., than No.2114 at the bottom of the bank in Durham Station. As a result of these tests, the relative haulage abilities of the North Eastern express classes were established at class 'R'

100, class 'S1' 105, class 'V' 128 and the four-cylinder compounds 145.

After Wordsell had retired in 1911, an order was placed for ten more compound similar to Nos.730 and 731, but, for some reason these were cancelled. A story exists that the executors of Smith's estate asked for very high royalties on the use of his patents. Vincent Raven, the newly appointed CME was not a notable enthusiast for compounding and, anyway, would presumably have pressed the virtues of his own design. This turned out to be the three-cylinder simple 'Z' class 'Atlantics', a very successful design which eclipsed the compounds in the years to follow. They lasted in service until 1933 and 1935.

One more North Eastern compound remains to be described, the remarkable *Aerolite*. This locomotive was originally built by the firm of Kitson, Thompson and Hewitson for the Leeds Northern, as long ago as 1851 as a 2-2-2 well tank. Edward Fletcher rebuilt her in 1869 and T. W. Wordsell in 1886, but as far as this record is concerned, the next re-building in 1892 is the significant one. Of course, it is extremely doubtful if much of the original locomotive survived these transformations, but the 1892 form was of a 4-2-2 two-cylinder compound side tank.

In 1902, the engine was turned around in the frames, probably to carry a larger bunker, to become the museum piece to be seen at York today. In her final form, the high-pressure cylinder has a diameter of 13in. and the low-pressure 18½in., both with a stroke of 20in. The low-pressure piston has a tail rod. The driving wheels are 5ft. 7in. and Stephenson link motion actuates the slide valves. The weight is given as 44 tons 9cwt.

From 1907, *Aerolite* was used exclusively by the Locomotive Department until 1926, when she was transferred back into normal operation. Presumably this was with the idea of working out the mileage prior to scrapping and she was used as a replacement for the self-propelled railcars at times. By the time of her withdrawal, in 1933, the museum at York was set up and there she rests. In common with the other three North Eastern single tanks, *Aerolite* was painted passenger green by the LNER, the only tank engines so honoured.

Details of the North Eastern compounds

Class 'C' 0-6-0
171 Built 1886-92.
Rebuilt as simples 1896-1912.
First locomotive withdrawn 1929; last locomotive withdrawn 1961.

Class 'B' 0-6-2T
51 built 1886-90.
Rebuilt as simples 1896-1910.
First locomotive withdrawn 1929; last locomotive withdrawn 1956.

Class 'D' 2-4-0
2 Built 11/1886 (No.1324) & 12/1888 (No.340).
Rebuilt as 4-4-0 class 'F1' simple October 1896.
Withdrawn December 1933 (No.340) and February 1930 (No.1324).

Class 'F' 4-4-0
10 Built:
6/1887 Nos.18, 42, 115.
1/1887 Nos.117, 355, 514, 779.
12/1887 Nos.1, 663, 684.
Rebuilt as simples 1900-1905.
First locomotive withdrawn 1929; last locomotive withdrawn 1935.

Class 'I' 4-2-2
10 Built:
1888 Nos.1329, 1330
1889 Nos.1326-28
1890 Nos.1527-31
Rebuilt as simples

Class 'J' 4-2-2
10 Built 1888-1889

Class 'M' 4-4-0
No.1619 built May 1893.
Rebuilt as '3CC' August 1898.
Withdrawn October 1930.

Class '4CC' 4-4-2
Nos.730, 731 built 1906.
First locomotive withdrawn 1933; last locomotive withdrawn 1935.

Aerolite 2-2-4T

Chapter 5

Lancashire & Yorkshire Railway

In 1886, John Aspinal became Chief Mechanical Engineer of the Lancashire & Yorkshire Railway. His arrival coincided with the building of the new works at Horwich to meet the needs of an expanding locomotive stock. In the main, but with the notable exception of the 2-4-2 radial tanks, his designs were improved versions of those of his predecessor, Barton-Wright. However, by 1898, his thoughts, in common with those of the CMEs of many other British railways began to turn to larger things. In August of that year, he embarked on two new large designs. One of these was the famous 'Highflier' 'Atlantic' and the other a new 0-8-0 freight locomotive. 130 of these were built between 1900 and 1908 and shared the same boiler, cylinders and motion as the 4-4-2s. They were destined to be his last design.

As built, they were massive and impressive. The 'Atlantic' cylinders were bored out to a diameter of 20in., with a stroke of 26in. Joy valve gear actuated flat valves, all, of course, between the frames. The boiler pressure was 175p.s.i. and the driving wheels 4ft. 6in. in diameter, giving a nominal tractive effort of 28,644lbs. The weight in working order was 53 tons 16cwt.

By 1907, George Hughes was in command at Horwich and he re-built one of the Aspinal locomotives, No.1452, as a four-cylinder compound and built ten new locomotives to the same design. The high-pressure cylinders, 15½in. x 26in., were outside and drove on the third axle and the low-pressure, inside, 22in. x 26in. Two sets of Joy valve gear was fitted; each set driving a high-pressure and low-pressure valve through a rocking lever. The high-pressure valves were piston and the low-pressure balanced slide valves. The boiler was the Aspinal standard, 4ft. 10in. in diameter, with a grate area of 26sq.ft. and a heating surface of 2,050sq.ft. There were 225, 2in. diameter tubes and the barrel was 13ft. between the tube plates. Unlike the 'Atlantics', because no superheater was contemplated, the smokebox was not recessed into the barrel. The round top firebox lay over the rear axle and had a flat grate just under 8ft. long. The skimpy Aspinal cab was perched at the rear and the ensemble was completed with an eight-wheel tender. The weight came out at 60 tons 16cwt.

Hughes designed his own system for admitting live steam to the low-pressure cylinders for starting. In each low-pressure steam chest, an auxiliary slide valve was fitted, connected to the reversing rod. When the reverser was in full gear, steam at full boiler pressure was fed to these valves and through them into the low-pressure cylinders. At the same time, it flowed into the high-pressure receiver and onto both sides of the high-pressure pistons, which were thus in equilibrium. When the engine was linked up to about 73%, these auxiliary valves shut off the live steam, both to the low-pressure and to the receiver, thus commencing compound working. It can be seen that this process was completely automatic and outside the control of the driver. On the original Aspinal 0-8-0s, steam reversers had been fitted, but these proved unpopular and troublesome in service and the compounds had a screw reverser with a vertical column. The driving wheels were spaced at 3ft. 11in., 3ft. 2in. and 3ft. 2in. A neat and compact front end kept the overhang to a reasonable amount and avoided the 'front heavy' look of the Webb four-cylinder 0-8-0s. The distance from the leading axle to the buffer beam was 7ft. 2in. A built up crank axle was used, but despite the Joy valve gear, which allowed more room between the frames, the bearings, in common with those on all the L&Y 0-8-0s, were on the small side and problems were experienced with 'hot boxes'.

Somewhat naturally, Hughes embarked on a comparison between the compounds and the Aspinal simple locomotives. This involved a comparison between the work of the compounds and eleven of the simples spread over 24 months between November 1907 and November 1909. The findings were presented by Hughes to the 1910 March meeting of the Institute of Mechanical Engineers, with Aspinal in the chair. The results, he said, showed a saving of 9% in coal consumption on the road and an overall saving, including lighting up etc., of 4.9%. Speeds were low, averaging about 8m.p.h. and utilisation very low. The compounds were in steam for only 57% of the total time, against 64% for the simples. Coal consumption comparison was as follows:

	Compounds	Simples
per train mile	86.75	95.27
per engine mile	59.25	60.67
per ton mile	0.185	0.205

Despite the savings, no more compounds were built for the L&Y and, perhaps significantly, no comparative maintenance costs were given. E. S. Cox gives a telling comment on these: "It must have been the experience of putting up the inside motion work on these engines on hot August afternoons which predisposed me against inside cylinders for the whole of my designing career". The compounds all lasted to be re-numbered by the LMS, but were broken up in 1926 and 1927. Some of the simples were also withdrawn at this time, but the last ones came into British Railways ownership and finally went in 1951. Perhaps some of the frames were better than others?

The original Aspinal simples were L&Y class 'Q1' and the compounds class 'Q2'. They were numbered as follows, with LMS numbers in brackets:

1452 (12760) 1471 (12761) 1472 (12762) 1473 (12763) 1474 (12764)
1475 (12765) 1476 (12766) 1477 (12767) 1478 (12768) 1479 (12769)
1480 (12770)

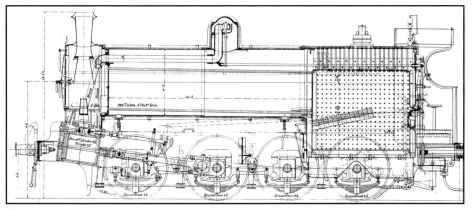

Hughes compound 0-8-0.

One more L&Y compound locomotive remains to be described, although not introduced until after the grouping. The original Hughes 4-6-0s of 1908 were as close to being total failures as any twentieth century locomotive class. Hughes gave a description of these engines in the paper to the Institute of Mechanical Engineers mentioned above and it is obvious that a great deal of thought and time was given to them. They were powerful engines with four 16in. by 26in. cylinders, a boiler with an outside diameter of 5ft. 10in., carrying a pressure of 180p.s.i. and with 6ft. 3in. driving wheels. Joy valve gear, all inside, actuated balanced slide valves lying over the cylinders. O. S. Nock suggests that all the effort was a monumental waste of time. All that could go wrong, it would seem, did. The coal consumption was astronomical, they would not run and were forever breaking down. With all the 'works' Inside, they were a fitter's nightmare and, with over half of them out of service in 1918, It was decided that nothing short of a complete re-design would do.

The second attempt was a little better. The boiler was retained and fitted with a high temperature superheater, but below the running board, all was new. Walschaerts valve gear now drove piston valves, set to give maximum travel of 6³/₈in. in full gear, but with only a moderate lap of 1³/₁₆in. This brought the coal consumption down from an astronomical 7lb. per draw bar horse power hour, to a less horrific, but still high, 5lbs. This was later reduced by fitting new piston valves to reduce leakage as the valves began to wear. Five of the earlier locomotives were scrapped without being modified, but a total of seventy of the new design were put into service, including fifteen re-builds. There were also ten identical engines built as 4-6-4 side tanks.

In the turmoil which attacked the locomotive department in the first years of the LMS, there were several abortive designs for larger motive power units which were vetoed by the all-powerful operating side. Besides the 4-6-0 three-cylinder compound project described elsewhere, there almost came to fruition two much larger machines. Almost immediately on George Hughes' retirement, a visit was made to France by Sir Henry Fowler and E. Gass, the Horwich Chief Draughtsman. Oliver Bullied was borrowed from the LNER to act as interpreter. Somewhat to their surprise, they did not find the French universally in favour of compounding, but the general consensus was that it saved about 15% in fuel bills, while adding only 8% to maintenance costs.

On their return, a start was made in laying out the designs for a four-cylinder 'Pacific' and a 2-8-2 freight locomotive with the same boiler and valve gear. The design was spread over the three main works; with Horwich dealing with the cylinders and valve gear, Derby with the boiler and Crewe with the other details.

The cylinders were to be placed in a line under the smokebox with the high-pressure outside; these had a diameter of 16¾in. and the low-pressure ones 23⅝in.; a common stroke of 26in. was to be adopted. Outside Walschaerts valve gear actuated the high-pressure valves, 9in. in diameter and the low-pressure pair, 11in. diameter, were to be driven through rocking levers. The belief that British drivers would be unable, or unwilling to used separate cut-offs effectively ruled out the provision of independent linking up. The 'Pacific' was to have the drive divided between the first and second axles, but in the 2-8-2, all the cylinders were to drive the second axle. The starting system was to be similar to that invented by George Hughes for his L&Y 0-8-0s.

The boiler was to be very large, 5ft. 9in. in outside diameter and, to keep the length between the tube plate to 17ft., a combustion chamber 4ft. in length was incorporated. There were to be 172 small tubes, 2⅛in. diameter, and 32 large tubes, 5⅛in. diameter. The wide firebox, with a grate area of 43½sq.ft., added a further 221sq.ft., giving an evaporative heating area of 2,578sq.ft. A high degree of superheat was aimed for, with an area of 631sq.ft. The working pressure was to be 240p.s.i.

The 'Pacific was to have 6ft. 9in. driving wheels and the freight locomotive 5ft. 3in., giving nominal tractive efforts of 34,600lbs. and 44,400lbs. respectively. The estimated weight for the 'Pacific' was 101 tons of which 63 tons rested on the driving wheels and a tender carrying 5½ tons of coal and 3,500 gallons of water was to be fitted. The 2-8-2 came out at 99 tons, 72 tons for adhesion and a larger tender, with a capacity of 8 tons of coal and 4,000 gallons of water, was designed.

While the design work was in progress, one of the last batch of Hughes 4-6-0s, No.10456, was converted into a four-cylinder compound to try out some of the principles behind the new engines in practice. New inside cylinders, 22in. in diameter, were fitted, while the outside, high-pressure pair was lined up to 15½in.

The 9in. piston valves were retained, as was the original boiler pressure of 180p.s.i. The rebuilt engine spent its working life between Crewe and Carlisle and on the heavy road, proved free running and was well liked by the crews. On test, it gave a saving of 26% in coal consumption over the standard 4-6-0s, but it must be said, that this fell to 9% when these locomotives were fitted with new piston valves to replace the original leaky ones.

Meanwhile, J. E. Andersen, Chief of Motive Power, which was an operations post and not connected with Fowler's department, was having misgivings about the new locomotives. He held the belief that the fewer cylinders and wheels that a locomotive possessed, the better. Furthermore, he was appalled at the cost in new turntables which would be needed if the new 'Pacific' was introduced. Anderson went to the senior management of the LMS, without reference to Fowler and persuaded them to ask Swindon for the loan of a 'Castle'. No.5000 *Launceston Castle* came to the LMS in September 1926 and proved the master of all that the operating authorities threw at her. On the Carlisle road, she "performed with quiet mastery all the work on which the 'Claughtons', often piloted, lost time, dropped their steam pressure, and made the welkin ring with their reverberating exhaust" (E. S. Cox, 'Locomotive Panorama').

At once, Fowler was ordered to stop work on his new designs and, despite the fact that some parts, flanging blocks, foundation rings and, probably some cylinders, had already been made for the first pair of 'Pacifics', the whole project was cancelled. The result was the order for the 50 'Royal Scots' from the North British Locomotive Company and, as these had three cylinders, Anderson would seem to have got his way.

The big compound 'Pacific' may have proved once and for all the possibilities of compounding in Britain, but it must be said that certain features in the design were, on the face of it, defective. They had bearings on the small side and the boiler was complicated; furthermore, they lacked the refinements to take full advantage of compounding as developed by Chapelon in France. But, a great chance to try the ultimate British compound locomotive was lost and the LMS had to wait another nine years for its first 'Pacific'.

Chapter 6
Great Northern Railway

H. A. Ivatt had experimented with compound propulsion during his stay at Inchicore on the Great Southern and Western Railway in Ireland. In 1894, he had re-built a 6ft. 7in. 4-4-0 and a 0-6-0 goods engine as two-cylinder compounds. The starting system on these locomotives incorporated a non-automatic 'triplex' valve, enabling the driver to admit live steam to the low-pressure steam chest. These engines were no better than the original simples, partly because of the low boiler pressure, only 150p.s.i. and partly because the 'triplex' valve very often stuck. The resulting flow of steam choked the low-pressure cylinder. Both were re-converted to two-cylinder simples in 1901.

By 1903, Ivatt was in the seat at Doncaster and his 'Atlantics', with their simple two-cylinder lay-out and in the case of No.251 and her large boilered successors, enormous steam raising capabilities were the masters of any task the Great Northern operating department could find for them. The valve events and steam cycle restrictions meant that this was achieved at the cost of some dramatically high coal consumptions. Even after a superheated boiler was fitted in 1923, the coal consumption of a large 'Atlantic' was found to be as high as 5.08lbs. per drawbar horsepower when hauling a 300 ton train at an average speed of 50m.p.h. In the face of some resistance from Ivatt himself, the Board instructed him, with Bury the general manager, to seek tenders from outside locomotive manufacturers for the construction of a compound 'Atlantic' for comparison with No.251. All the tendered designs were either too heavy, or too long and Ivatt recommended that no further action be taken on the matter. Bury, however, disagreed and on his advice the Vulcan Foundry was given the order to supply a compound 'Atlantic' "of the de Glehn type" to the Great Northern. It would appear that the specification went little further than that, for it is apparent from the finished article that the builders had a totally free hand in the design.

The boiler, although not fitted with a wide firebox, was virtually as large as Ivatt's own product. Indeed, because of the massive round-topped firebox, reminiscent, because of its larger diameter than the boiler barrel, of a design from Swindon of twenty years earlier, the total heating surface was actually 14sq.ft. more. French practice was followed in the use of ribbed 'Servre' tubes, of which 149 were fitted. The high-pressure cylinders, outside, were placed between the bogie and the leading pair of driving wheels and drove the rear pair. The leading driving wheels were in turn, driven by the low-pressure, inside cylinders, which were located at the front of the frames. The cylinders were of conventional compound proportions, 14in.

GNR compound 'Atlantic' No.1300, built by Vulcan Foundry in 1905, following rebuild as a two-cylinder simple in 1917.

and 23in. diameter, with a common stroke of 26in. This gave a volumetric relationship of about 2.6:1. Separate sets of Walschaert gear actuated the valves, piston for the high-pressure and balanced slide valves for the low-pressure and independent cut-off adjustment was possible. The Vulcan Foundry fitted a number of their own patent devices, including a starting valve, which admitted live steam at reduced pressure to the low-pressure cylinders and closed automatically when the receiver pressure increased and a combined screw reversing lever, which allowed the driver to link up the valves together if he wished.

It was too much to expect that Ivatt's considerable professional pride would allow the Vulcan 'Atlantic' to have the field to itself and he lost no time in preparing the designs for his own compound. However, he was, at that time, under considerable pressure of work on other matters and after the preliminary designs had been prepared, he was forced by ill health, to take leave of absence and to go to Italy for a rest. As a result, the actual production work fell to the lot of Earl Marsh, but just before it took the road, he was off to Brighton as the new Chief Mechanical Engineer. The new assistant, Wintour, finally got No.292, as the compound had become, into service.

The new locomotive was a four-cylinder 'Smith' type compound, that is with the cylinders in a line under the smokebox, high-pressure outside and low-pressure between the frames. Ivatt's famous premise that a locomotive's capacity could be measured by its ability to boil water, led him to provide adequate boiler size. The standard large boiler was fitted and, with a total heating surface of no less than 2,500sq.ft., coupled with a grate area of 31sq.ft., there was unlikely to be any shortage of steam. What is more, in order to take advantage of the extra expansive possibilities of the compound engine, he gave No.292 a boiler pressure of 200p.s.i., as against the 150p.s.i. of the simple 'Atlantics'.

The high-pressure cylinders drove the rear coupled wheels and had balanced slide valves above, actuated by Walschaerts gear; the low-pressure valves were between the cylinders, which drove the front coupled wheels and were driven by Stephenson link motion. A steam servo-driven change valve was fitted to give the driver the choice of compound, or simple working and also, of course, for starting. There were two reversing levers on the footplate which could be linked up, either independently, or together, again as the driver wished. The coupled wheels were 6ft. 7½in. in diameter and the locomotive weighed 69 tons, of which 36½ tons was available for adhesion. It was the designers' predilection for small cylinders, which proved the stumbling block in this design. The high-pressure cylinders were only 13in. in diameter with the very short stroke of 20in. and the low-pressure ones were 16in. x 26in. The tiny high-pressure cylinders made No.292 a very weak starter and the volumetric ratio of only 1.99:1 resulted in a choked receiver when running. Furthermore, the different valve events produced by the outside radial gear and the inside link motion as the engine was linked up, would add to this.

The third excursion of the Great Northern into the compound 'Atlantic' field came in 1907 with No.1421. Again, all four cylinders were in a line under the smokebox and this time piston valves actuated by Walschaerts gear were used for both high-pressure and low-pressure. The low-pressure cylinders were the same as the standard two-cylinder 'Atlantics', that is, 18in. x 26in., but Ivatt kept the same diminutive high-pressure ones as on No.292. Divided drive was again used and, as a result, the inside connecting rods were very short.

The boiler was, in a sense, a cross between those of the small and large 'Atlantics', in that it had the wide firebox of the latter, but the recessed smokebox of the former. This resulted in a total heating surface of 2,352sq.ft., a reduction of 150sq.ft. when compared with the standard large 'Atlantic' boiler. The chimney was set well forward on the smokebox which gave a rather curiously foreshortened appearance.

Before No.1421 was built, a series of tests were carried out to compare the work of the first two compounds with that of a standard large 'Atlantic'. No.294 had her boiler pressure raised to 200p.s.i. for the occasion, to produce a fair comparison. In other cases of tests between simple and compound locomotives, the apparent

Ivatt's compound 'Atlantic' No.1421 of 1907.

fuel saving by the compounds could often be accounted for by the higher boiler pressure alone. It depends what you are trying to prove! Three crews were used and after a week of familiarisation, they each had charge of a locomotive for three weeks. As far as I can trace, the period of nine weeks continuous trial is the longest comparison made between different locomotive types on test in this country. It is a pity that they were not carried out over a greater range of working conditions, as the results might then have been more conclusive.

Ivatt presented the results to the Institute of Mechanical Engineers in May 1907 and the results were so similar as to be indistinguishable from each other. The two-cylinder 'Atlantic' was cheapest in maintenance costs, No.292 had the lowest fuel consumption by a small margin and the Vulcan came out worst, albeit by a very small amount overall. However, with train loads averaging only 250 tons, these investigations was no great test for any of them.

The results of these tests and the indifferent performance of the later locomotive did not persuade Ivatt to pursue his compound experiments. One of the requisites of any compound engine is large low-pressure cylinder volume and Ivatt did not believe in large cylinders; had he fitted his compounds with cylinders of a size more in keeping with their boiler capacity, the performance might have been a different story. Nigel Gresley, in his early years at least, was no fan of compounding and although he fitted No.1421 with a 22 row superheater in 1914, he wasted no time in rebuilding both her and the Vulcan as two-cylinder simples after the First World War; No.1421 became a standard large 'Atlantic' and No.1300 was given a pair of standard 'K2' 20in. x 26in. cylinders. No.292 soldiered on as a compound until her withdrawal in 1927.

Details of the Great Northern compounds

Four-cylinder 4-4-2 No.292
Built Doncaster 1905.
Withdrawn 1927.

Four-cylinder 4-4-2 No.1300
Built Vulcan Foundry 1905.
Rebuilt two-cylinder simple 1917.
Withdrawn 1924.

Four-cylinder 4-4-2 No.1421
Built Doncaster 1907.
Rebuilt with superheated boiler 1914.
Rebuilt as standard two-cylinder simple 1920.

Chapter 7

London & South Western Railway

It was a tradition throughout the life of the London & South Western Railway to build express locomotives with different diameter driving wheels for use east and west of Salisbury. When William Adams came to the L&SW in 1878, his first tender design, the '135' class, was fitted with 6ft. 7in. driving wheels for the western section. He followed this, in 1883, with a second class, the '445', with 7ft. 1in. driving wheels for the eastern. The latter had two outside cylinders, 18in. x 24in. and were very free running and efficient engines. At first, they were all stationed at Nine Elms for working the best Bournemouth and Salisbury expresses and it was unusual, but not unknown, to find them west of Salisbury.

In common with other engineers in the 1880s, Adam's thoughts turned to compounding as a method of saving coal and he looked with interest at the first Webb compounds, then in 1884 being turned out from Crewe with much publicity. In March of that year, he approached Webb to ask for the loan of a L&NW compound, together with a crew, to try on the South Western. Webb was only too pleased to oblige and in May, sent No.300 *Compound*. This was the original Webb locomotive and was of about the same nominal power as the Adams '445' class. It did not cover itself with glory. The performance up the banks west of Salisbury was up to the best South Western standard, but it proved quite incapable of the high speed down the other side, needed to keep time. The loads were not heavy, only 150 tons to Salisbury and 110 tons from there to Exeter and the 11a.m. Down, later to be the much lamented 'Atlantic Coast Express', was allowed 4 hours 13 minutes, with six stops for the 171 miles. The running average speed, exclusive of stops, was therefore, about 43m.p.h. and this and the corresponding 10.05a.m. Up train proved beyond the compounds' capabilities. Moreover, time was lost in starting from the stations, sometimes taking up to five minutes to get the double single under way. Far from showing economy in coal consumption, the compound burned 36lbs. of coal per mile as against a figure of 26lbs. for the '445' and '135' classes on similar work. However, 'burned', in the case of the compound, may be the wrong word, because No.300 had to be thrashed so hard in the attempt to keep time that much of the coal finished up burning in the smokebox, or in the lineside fields. In June No.300 was returned to Crewe with thanks and no doubt, some relief.

Adams does not seem to have been put off compounding *per se*, perhaps just the Webb system, for in 1886 his mind turned even further north, to the North Eastern, where T. W. Wordsell, having absorbed the lessons of his Great Eastern locomotives, had just introduced the first of his North Eastern compounds with a flourish. Adams decided to try a two-cylinder compound and applied to his Locomotive Committee for permission to convert one of the '445' class to the Wordsell-Von Borries system. This he got, with the proviso that the cost did not exceed £200.

'445' class No.446 while running as a compound between 1888 and 1891.

The re-built locomotive, No.446, came into service in February 1888, fitted with a new right-hand cylinder with a diameter of 26in. A larger hole was cut in the frames to accommodate this, but it was only the large driving wheels and the fact that the connecting rods on these locomotives were inside the coupling rods that made the experiment possible. Even so, some of the platform clearances were pretty tight. The Stephenson link motion was modified to give longer travel to the low-pressure cylinder and double ported valves were fitted to both cylinders. The boiler pressure remained at 160p.s.i. During its life as a compound, No.446 carried an oval brass plate on the cabside announcing that the Wordsell-Von Borries compound system was fitted.

Some comparative trials were carried out with No.448 of the same class and Adams reported the results to the Locomotive Committee in December 1890. They were so close as to be indistinguishable from each other. The compound burned 29.68lbs. of coal per mile and the simple 27.4lbs. After this inconclusive result, No.446 remained as a compound for only one more year, running a total of 63,272 miles and was re-built into its original state in 1891. The locomotive was finally withdrawn from service in May 1925.

Class '445' 4-4-0 No. 446
Built April 1883 by R. Stephenson & Co.
Rebuilt as compound February 1888.
Rebuilt as simple February 1891.
Withdrawn May 1925.

Chapter 8
Midland Railway

If success is measured solely by numbers, then the Johnson, Deeley, Fowler Midland locomotives were by far the most effective in Britain. The first two were built at Derby in 1902 and were to all purposes an enlargement of the North Eastern Smith three-cylinder rebuild of T. W. Wordsell's Class 'M' 4-4-0 No.1619. They had all the features described in the North Eastern chapter, except cross water tubes in the firebox. This may have been in no small measure due to the fact that Walter Smith's eldest son was employed at Derby and that Wilson Wordsell and Johnson were good friends. The co-operation between Derby and Gateshead was unique in an age when locomotive works were secretive places and drawing offices even more so. The development of the Smith piston valves had been carried out on a joint basis and it was not surprising that Derby took an interest in the working of No.1619. As was to be expected of a design so different from anything seen on the Midland before, Nos.2631 and 2632 were subjected to a comprehensive series of tests in the first year of their existence. As originally built, the arrangement to allow of their working as simples when the severity of the work demanded, differed from the later, standard, system. A regulating valve, located on the right-hand side of the smokebox, admitted live steam to the low-pressure steam chest; when the pressure on the low-pressure piston reached a pre-determined level, the same valve automatically cut off this supply. When working compound, the low-pressure steam chest pressure was found to be between 40-60p.s.i. The valve gear provided for independent adjustment of the high-pressure and low-pressure cut-offs, although a combination lever allowed for alteration to both gears simultaneously, when required. Thus, the locomotives had a multiplicity of controls comparable to those of the de Glehn system. A further non-return valve between the high-pressure and low-pressure valve chests prevented excessive back pressure on the high-pressure pistons when starting. A large 'Belpaire' boiler was fitted based on that on the successful class '3' two-cylinder simples.

The cylinders, with a common stroke of 26in., had diameters of 19in. high-pressure and 21in. low-pressure. The steam distribution was by a piston valve on the high-pressure side and slide valves working on vertical faces in the case of the low-pressure cylinders. The high-pressure exhaust was fed directly into the common low-pressure steam chest, without the use of any intermediate piping. Stephenson's link motion drove all three valves. The boiler was a very large one for a 4-4-0 in 1902; for the first time, the Midland produced a locomotive with the boiler capacity of a 'Dunalistair', South Western 'T9', or North Eastern 'R'. The total

Johnson compound No.2632, Built at Derby in 1902.

heating surface was 1,600sq.ft. in a barrel 11ft. 7in. long and 4ft. 8in. in diameter, but the most significant feature was a grate area of no less than 26sq.ft. The boiler pressure was 195p.s.i.

With the large bogie tenders, which carried 4,500 gallons of water and 3½ tons of coal, the new engines were most handsome and the tests carried out between Leeds and Carlisle proved that the beauty was not only skin deep. The Midland had no dynamometer car at that time and so indicated rather than drawbar, horsepower, was used as the datum.

As the adjustment of the controls was left entirely in the hands of the driver, it is of particular interest to consider the method of operation. A maximum indicated horsepower of 1,001½ was achieved at a speed of 37m.p.h. just at Ais Gill on an Up train weighing 248 tons. The cut-off was set at 63% high-pressure and 57% low-pressure and the regulating valve was partly open, so some live steam was being used by the low-pressure cylinders. These cut-off positions and others used during the tests, relate very closely to those used when the independent adjustments were removed. Over on the North Western two years later, the Whale 'Precursor' produced 1,168 indicated horsepower at the same speed, while accelerating south of Crewe; the 'Precursors' proved capable of sustained power outputs of about 1,000 indicated horsepower at 60 miles per hour. However, the cut-offs used in the case of the compound, were the equivalent of only about 25% in a simple expansion engine and given the North Western methods of operation in 1905, it is likely that 40% would be nearer their mark. In 1902, no attempt was made to ascertain the absolute maximum output of the compound and although the load was a heavy one for the time, it was light compared with those taken in later years. Of course, although the ability of the cylinders to use the steam is of prime importance in the business of spot power output, it is the efficacy of the boiler to produce the steam which determines whether this power can be maintained for any length of time. Only on one occasion during these particular tests was this put to trial; the fifteen mile climb from Ormslde Viaduct up to Ais Gill summit was taken with the cut-off set at 69% high-pressure and 70% low-pressure and with the regulating valve open some of the time. The boiler pressure and water level was maintained against the use of both injectors and the indicated horsepower was about 1,200.

In normal express service, some very impressive performances were recorded over the same road. Both the locomotives when new, were stationed at Leeds, but by the summer of 1902, No.2632 was at Durranhill, the Midland shed at Carlisle for the tests. In between tests, they worked the normal express traffic over Blea Moor and Ais Gill. Two runs were timed by Rous-Marten, one with each locomotive, which were notable. The first, on the evening of 5th September, featured No.2631 on the Down afternoon 'Scotch' express; this was a heavy train, 282 tons tare from Leeds. After Hellifield, where 53 tons were detached, No.2631 was given her head. Speed had risen to 60m.p.h. by Settle Junction and the subsequent working was hard enough to keep the speed up to 35m.p.h. at the summit between Ribblehead and Blea Moor. The boiler was steaming perfectly and the fireman was obviously fit and so there was no easing on the descent. The average speed over the 17½ miles from Ais Gill to Appleby was 75m.p.h., with a maximum of 86m.p.h. at Kirkby Stephen. The final 30.8 miles of this fine run were covered at an average speed of 68.4m.p.h., with the notable minimum of 55m.p.h. at Lazonby and another 80m.p.h. at Little Salkeld.

At the time, that is late 1902, the railways of Britain were coming to the end of the craziest seventeen years in the history of transport. Starting in 1888, with the race to Edinburgh and ending in the early hours of 1st July 1906, was an era which saw the normally sober, hard-headed gentlemen of the railway management, indulge in out-and-out racing, racing, moreover, with trains carrying fare paying passengers. When G. J. Churchward told Inspector Flewellen of the Great Western that "he could go and break his bloody neck", he was risking the neck of others as well. When the South Western Plymouth Boat Train hit the parapet of the road bridge at Salisbury on that July morning, it "Slammed the door on any further acceleration of train service in Britain for many years to come".

Before this happened, there were two runs in particular, which stand out as achievements considerably above the norm. One was the flight of *City of Truro* and *Duke of Connaught* with the 'Ocean Mails' from Plymouth to Paddington and the other, which is part of this story and rather less well known, was further North. The Midland authorities allowed it to be 'leaked' to the technical press in the Autumn of 1903, that one of their locomotives had hauled a train at "considerably over 90 miles per hour". The train in question was the 11:50a.m. Up 'Scotch Express' from Carlisle and Rous-Marten was again a passenger and his presence would seem to have had some connection with what took place. Certainly, it would seem that Driver Killan was aware that he was on the train. The performance on the day in question was probably the finest ever seen on this line, taking into consideration the load and the locomotive.

The bare facts are that Killan and his fireman took No.2632, with a load of 240 tons, over the 48.3 miles, uphill, from Carlisle to Ais Gill in 57 minutes 38 seconds, an average speed of 57m.p.h. During the course of the climb, the maximum speed was 72m.p.h. at Lazonby, but even more notable, was the time from Appleby to Ais Gill, 17½ miles in 23 minutes 5 seconds and a minimum speed up the final 1:100 of 43m.p.h. After Blea Moor, the train was run at high speed down the bank to such effect that 80m.p.h. was reached at Ribblehead, that is within two miles of the summit. On the descent through Ribblesdale, Rous Marten timed successively two quarter miles at exactly ten seconds, that is 90m.p.h., one at 9.8 seconds (91.8m.p.h.) and finally one at 9.4 seconds, (96m.p.h.). The 86.8 miles to Skipton were covered in 93 minutes 18 seconds, an average speed of 55.8m.p.h. There is a story, which has been passed down over the years, which perhaps shows that official sanction had not been given for this bit of record breaking; the traffic department at Leeds became aware of the speed of the train and proceeded to bring the record to an end by the simple expedient of diverting some ten slow trains onto the Fast line down the Aire Valley. Rous-Marten estimated that this added about 21 minutes to the running time and but for this, Leeds would have been reached in under two hours from Carlisle. The actual time was 2 hours 16 minutes 47 seconds.

The importance of this run, in the light of the subsequent history of the Midland compounds, is that the speed reached by No.2632 was the highest ever recorded by a member of the class in its sixty years of service, moreover, No.2632 was, at the time, still fitted with the original, saturated, boiler. In the hands of the small number of top drivers, the multiplicity of controls for the valve gear presented no problems, but presumably Johnson had doubts about its suitability for general use, for in his next batch of compounds, he abandoned the independent cut-offs in favour of a fixed ratio. This altered the effective relationship between the volume of the high-pressure and low-pressure cylinders as the valve gear was linked up, resulting in choking of the low-pressure receiver, especially when the engine was being worked hard at longer cut-offs and, while not affecting the power output, put a restraint on the speed capabilities of the locomotives. On the downhill sections of the Settle and Carlisle line, the drivers of Nos.2631 and 2632 set the low-pressure cut-off to a later value than the high-pressure; in the combined gear, the low-pressure cut-off was about 10% of the stroke earlier than the high-pressure side. O. S. Nock has recalled a conversation he had with a very well informed and keen LMS express driver from Wakefield shed. He had experience of both two-cylinder and three-cylinder Stanier 4-6-0s, Midland Class '2' 4-4-0s and of the compounds. These were great favourites of his, but his telling comment was, "I wish they had independent cut-offs like the French do. They could run much faster like that". The strict limits imposed on the loads on the Midland Railway meant that the compounds could run so fast up the banks that no exceptional downhill speed was necessary. Neverthless, even with the later advantages of superheated steam, no other record exists of a Midland compound exceeding 85 miles per hour.

The second batch of compounds were built during Johnson's last year in office, 1903; No.2633 in July, No.2634 in September and No.2635 in November. These three were shedded at Kentish Town to work the best expresses from St Pancras. As well as the changes in the valve gear, they differed from Nos.2631 and 2632 in that the low-pressure cylinders were fixed below the unbroken line of the footplate, whereas the earlier two had the cylinders projecting through the plating. All five were fitted with double bogie 'water cart' tenders holding 5 tons of coal and 4,500 gallons of water.

When S. W. Johnson retired at the end of 1903, it was in the midst of a general and total re-organisation of the affairs of the Midland Railway. The two men in the Locomotive Department who were in line to succeed Johnson, were Richard Mountford Deeley, the Works Manager and Cecil Paget, his assistant. Deeley had served his pupilage under Johnson and had risen through the ranks of the Locomotive Department. Paget was a man of outstanding ability and who was, moreover, the son of the Chairman of the Company. It was widely thought that Paget would succeed to the post and indeed *The Locomotive Magazine* noted in the September 1903 edition that, "Mr. Cecil Paget has been appointed to succeed Mr. S. W. Johnson". Despite this, it was Deeley who became Locomotive Superintendent of the Midland Railway at the start of 1904.

In 1906, there came an appointment of even more significance to the Midland Railway. The Directors gave the post of General Manager to W. G. Granet. Granet was a barrister and so brought a new mind into the organisation that was not biased by preconceived ideas on railway organisation. This was immediately apparent in the new structure which he set up. To the fore of this, was the new office of General Superintendent, among whose responsibilities was the running of the locomotives. Deeley's job was re-designated Chief Mechanical Engineer and his functions limited to design, construction and repair. The new Superintendent was Cecil Paget.

One of the first results of the new system was a general renumbering of locomotives in which the number gave an indication of the power category. Thus, the Johnson compounds became Nos.1000-4 and Deeleys, of which more anon, had 5 added to their numbers and so became 1005 etc. More important, however, was the assumption by the Traffic Department under this scheme, that any locomotive within a power class, irrespective of its condition, could keep time with the load appropriate to that class. Load limits were set for each power class for every duty; if the actual load exceeded this by as much as one ton, then an assisting locomotive was provided. The 'Special Limit' load for the compounds as power class 4 was 230 tons. Across the road at Euston, the 'Precursors' were taking twice the load on the 'Scotch Expresses'.

Before all this happened, Deeley had been so impressed by the outstanding achievements of the Johnson compounds, that he pressed the Board of Directors in the spring of 1904 for authority to build forty more, fitted with superheated boilers. Even in the days before the great re-organisation, capital outlay was strictly limited and Deeley was given permission only to take "exploratory action". This resulted in an order for ten new compounds and by the Autumn he reported that the Scmidt organisation required a large sum of money per boiler in royalties for the use of their patents. As a result of this added cost, Deeley was ordered to build his compounds with saturated steam.

It was in this atmosphere that Deeley produced his version of the Johnson-Smith compound. The first ten appeared at the end of 1905; the numbers were, at first, 1000-1009, but soon afterwards became 1005-1014. Their outward design differed quite sharply from their predecessors. Gone were the ugly, square rear splashers, but so had the brass beading and brass safety-valve covers. On the other hand, a shapely chimney returned and, for the first time on the Midland, a canopied cab was provided. Internally, the differences were even more significant. The grate area was increased to 28.4sq.ft. and the boiler pressure to 220p.s.i. The tube heating surface was reduced, which seems to have improved the steaming of the boiler. The tractive effort went up from the 19,110lbs of the Johnson locomotives, to 21,560lbs. Water troughs had been installed on the Midland by the time these locomotives were built, at Melton Mowbray, Loughborough and Oakley and a further set, in 1907, high in the hills of the Settle-Carlisle line at Hawes Junction. These made the big bogie tenders unnecessary and a standard six-wheel tender was fitted to these and subsequent compounds. A further twenty compounds were built in 1906, which differed again in appearance, having shallower frames at the front end so that the smokebox saddle did not extend onto the forward footplate, but had a more modern, short aspect. On all these locomotives, a control system totally different from the Smith principle was fitted.

As has been seen, Johnson, in his second batch of compounds abandoned the independent cut-off for the high-pressure and low-pressure valve gear, but retained the Smith starting system. Deeley found that there were frequent failures of the reducing valve and so he designed a regulator which made this unnecessary. It had two valves, one of which admitted live steam to the low-pressure valves through a small diameter pipe for use when starting. Thus, the locomotive started as a two-cylinder simple. As the regulator was opened progressively, steam began to be fed to the high-pressure valve. When the train was moving, the regulator was opened fully, the small valve closed and the main steam feed was directed to the high-pressure cylinder. The small valve would remain closed in all further movements of the regulator and it was impossible to revert to semi-compound working unless the regulator was fully closed, so full compound working could be maintained even with the regulator 'cracked'. The regulator was simple and accurate to use and was

The first of Deeley's compounds, No.1000, renumbered in 1907 to 1005.

popular with the crews, but it did not allow the driver to control the semi-compound working with the same finess that the Smith reducing valve provided.

Despite the fact that some of the train timings were quite sharp, in particular the 105 minutes for the 99 miles from Leicester to St. Pancras, the loads on the 'Special Limit' were so light that the compounds were never really extended and speeds in excess of 70m.p.h. downhill were rare.

In 1906, the North British Railway borrowed one of the Deeley compounds to work on the Waverley route, in comparison with one of their own two-cylinder simple 'Atlantics' and one of the Smith four-cylinder compound 'Atlantics' of the North Eastern Railway. Apparently, the North British management was not satisfied with its newest express locomotive and wished to compare it with the two most efficient classes at work on the northern lines at that time. No.1032 carried herself with honour, if not exactly with glory.

As a result of the success of the 4-4-0s, Deeley had sought permission to build the last five of the order as 'Atlantics', but this was refused. In 1908, Paget had built, at his own expense, at Derby his famous 2-6-2 locomotive with all its unique features. It was not to be expected that, in the atmosphere of the Midland at the time, that Deeley would let this go unanswered. His own design was for a four-cylinder compound tank engine, with the wheels arranged as 2-4-4-2, with the high-pressure cylinders under the bunker, driving the rear pair of axles and the low-pressure set in the conventional position driving the front pair. The same boiler as the 4-4-0 compounds was to be fitted and the cylinders were to be 13in. x 26in. high-pressure and 20in. x 26in. low-pressure. Steam distribution was to be by 8¾in. diameter piston valves to the high-pressure cylinders and slide valves to the low-pressure side, all driven by Walschaerts gear. Coupled wheel diameter was 5ft. and, with a Bissel truck at each end, the total wheel base was 37ft. Tank capacity was to be 2,000 gallons and 3½ tons of coal were provided. Quite what sort of work was imagined for this extraordinary ensemble is not known. The layout would not seem to be suitable for high-speed work and, if the Deeley regulator was fitted, on starting, the high-pressure cylinders would not be provided with steam and the resulting loss of traction would not be suitable for heavy freight work.

Another project, drawings dated November 1907, was for a 4-6-0 compound on the de Glehn, rather than the Smith system. The projected weight was 76 tons for the locomotive alone and would have been the largest express passenger engine in Britain. The boiler was to have a heating surface of 1,970sq.ft. and 30sq.ft. of grate area; piston valves of 8¾in. diameter were to be fitted and the valve gear was to be of the 'scissors' type, as used by Churchward on *North Star* and Deeley on the '990' class. This gear, which has no eccentrics, was much used in stationary engines and took up less room between the frames. The motion is derived from the opposite cylinder, through rocking levers and it is this, supposed, disadvantage which prevented further use. The big 4-6-0 should have been hauling loads of 400 tons on the 'Special Limit' timings, but the operating authorities would have none of it and the project got no further than the drawing office.

The need to contain expenses and the ease with which the compounds dealt with the 'Special Limit' timings, led Deeley in 1907, to build a class of two-cylinder 4-4-0 simples. These had the same boiler as the compounds, but a slight re-arrangement of the tubes gave an extra 90 sq. ft. of heating surface, 19in. x 26in. cylinders and 6ft. 6in. diameter driving wheels. The scissors valve gear was fitted, but Deeley stuck to the traditional valve settings. With hindsight, it seems remarkable that even as inventive an engineer as Deeley, could not appreciate the value of long travel, long lap valves, but he did not and the '999' class was, perhaps, a lost opportunity. There is no record of any comparative testing of the two classes in Deeley's time, but the fact that more compounds were built In 1908 would indicate that the '999' were the less successful, even at the outset.

Deeley's departure from Derby in 1909 was accompanied, as is often the case when strong personalities are involved, by drama. One story is told in which he stormed into the works, accompanied by a fitter carrying a bag of tools who, while Deeley stood by, removed the name plate from his office door. Deeley turned on his heel and left Derby, never to return. He lived to the age of 89 years, but devoted the rest of his life to science.

He was succeeded by Henry Fowler, another engineer of first-class intellect, but a man possessing what Deeley did not, that is the ability to work as a member of Granert's team. Thus, the rebuilding of the class '2' and '3' 4-4-0 locomotives had priority over the establishment of a really effective class 4 stud, for which, in any case, the operating authorities had little use. The only development of the compounds during Fowler's occupation of the chair at Derby until the formation of the LMS, was the provision of superheated boilers, beginning with No.1040 in 1914. However, it is apparent that Derby considered superheating as an alternative to compounding, because the whole of the '999' class was so treated before even three of the compounds. Tests were carried out in 1910 between No.998, fitted with a superheater and a standard, saturated compound No.1043 and in 1913, between two of the compounds, No.1039, saturated and No.1040, superheated. Fowler, in a paper to the Institute of Civil Engineers, reported that the tests showed that a reduction in coal consumption of no less than 25.9% was achieved by the superheated locomotive. It is certainly puzzling in the light of these results that, even by the time of the grouping, only twenty-four of the compounds had been fitted with superheated boilers. These included the original Johnson engines, which were rebuilt to conform in outward appearance, as well as with the starting and regulator gear with the later Deeley compounds. The boiler pressure of these engines was reduced from 220p.s.i. to 190p.s.i. between 1916 and 1918 to save on maintenance costs.

So, at the formation of the LMS, the Midland contributed 45 compound 4-4-0s, which, even when fitted with superheated boilers, would seem to have been inferior in performance to the L&NW 'George V' class, let alone to the 'Claughton', or the Hughes L&Y class '8' 4-6-0. What is more, problems had arisen with the steaming of the superheated boilers which, when combined with the lower boiler pressure, was leading to frequent loss of time between Manchester and Derby, even with the 'Special Limit' loads. The measures adopted by Derby to overcome these failings were not calculated to improve the efficiency of the locomotives. Firstly, a valve was fitted to allow the driver to admit live steam to the low-pressure valve chests as he wished. This was a return to the Smith idea, albeit in a simpler form; it was merely a stop cock control. Secondly, the lap of the high-pressure valve was reduced from $1^{1}/_{16}$in. to $^{11}/_{16}$in; this was calculated to increase the power output and to even up the work done in each cylinder.

The organisation of the LMS in 1923 was most definitely based on the Midland pattern. Although George Hughes of the Lancashire & Yorkshire was the new Chief Mechanical Engineer, Fowler, who had been awarded KBE for his war work in 1918, so now was Sir Henry, was his deputy. The redoubtable Granert, who had masterminded the whole amalgamation, ensured that it was a Midland man, John Follows, who became the General Superintendent of the LMS. So, the precepts of Derby, rather than Crewe, reigned supreme. Prejudice against the products of Crewe and Horwich was illustrated by the locomotive power classifications; the compounds and the Deeley '990' class were given class '4', with the 'Prince of Wales' 4-6-0s but, significantly, the 'George Vs' were put into class '3'. Now, there is no doubt that in the matter of power output the compounds could run the 'Georges' pretty close but, as events were to show, the '990s' were not in the same category. In 1923, came the first of the comparative tests to be held to establish the future express passenger locomotive policy of the new company. These were held in December 1923 on the Leeds to Carlisle road and were officially 'to ascertain the comparative coal, water, and oil consumptions and engine performance of the three engines'. The three engines selected were the ex-LNWR 'Prince of Wales' No.388 and the two Midland 4-4-0s, No.998 and, what has been described as the best of the Midland compounds, by now fitted with a superheated boiler, No.1008. The test trains were those of the 'limited load' category and, with the timings allowed, were loaded to 260 tons.

In the event, the trains were loaded to 300 and 350 tons and how the Midland operating authorities were persuaded to permit such loads is something of a mystery. All the engine men entered into the tests with great enthusiasm and the North Western crew had worked over the road for some time beforehand. The first significant result of these tests was the total eclipse of the 4-4-0 simple No.998. With the runs hauling 350 tons, No.998 became very short of steam and on the last run, lost time to the extent of 3 minutes 15 seconds over the 11.2 miles from Blea Moor to Ais Gill. The performance of the other two locomotives was very impressive and, although the 'Prince' put up a slightly higher power output than the compound, it was at the expense of higher coal consumption. What then of No.1008? If it had been suggested to the Midland Railway that a train of 350 tons should be taken single-handed from Carlisle to Leeds, let alone that it would clear Ais Gill summit in 68 minutes from the start, a shudder of disbelief would have filled the corridors of Derby. The running of No.1008 in these tests represented the peak achievement of the Midland compounds; on the 18th December, the train, loaded to 370 tons gross, passed Ais Gill in 64½ minutes from Carlisle and a maximum drawbar horsepower of 1,025 was registered in the dynamometer car. At the same time, the coal consumption was no more than 46lbs per mile, which works out at 3.83lbs per drawbar horsepower. The firing rates were very high, probably reaching 150lbs per square foot of grate area per hour on the climb.

Northbound, the work was equally impressive, although on one run, No.1008 blew out a high-pressure steam gland. Probably the best run of the whole series was from Leeds to Carlisle with a train of 300 tons. The time of 71 minutes from Leeds to Blea Moor was two minutes inside the schedule and the coal consumption was only 3.64lbs per draw bar horse power. These results, when taken alongside the valve gear trouble that the 'Princes' were having at the time, confirmed to the all-powerful operating department of the LMS that the Midland compound was to be the basis of the future express passenger locomotive for the whole system.

Even before the results of these tests had been completed, an order for twenty new compounds was placed at Derby and when the analysis was complete, another order for twenty more was put in hand. These Fowler locomotives differed from the original Midland ones in several details. Numbered from Nos.1045-1064 and 1065-1084, they had the driving wheels reduced to 6ft. 9in. diameter and all the cylinders increased in diameter by ¾in. While these were under construction, a standard compound, No.1033, was sent to the North Western section to work the Birmingham two hour expresses and was considered to be successful enough to result in six of the new engines being allocated to this work. The ex-North Western crews did not, by and large, get the best out of these locomotives and the performances were generally not as good as the 'George V' class on the same road.

The way that the influence of the compounds was spreading, was illustrated by the fact that the second batch of twenty had the boiler mountings cut down, to enable them to work over lines in Scotland. The powers of the LMS were becoming so confident in their ability, that they set up yet another series of comparative trials over the Settle and Carlisle road in November 1924. The combatants this time were a 'Claughton', a Caledonian Class '3' 4-4-0 and the compounds. The Caley locomotive was totally incapable of hauling the 300 ton loads on the high hills and the 'Claughton', sent from Edge Hill shed at Liverpool, was not in the best of condition and steamed badly throughout the trial. Three compounds were used, two of the new Fowler locomotives and a standard '7' superheated engine. The contrast between these tests and that with No.1008 in the previous year is illuminating. The standard engine, No.1023, was unimpressive, particularly in the uphill work; time was lost to the extent of 28 minutes in total from Settle Junction to Ais Gill and it is evident that the load of 350 tons, overtaxed the locomotive. The two new compounds did better and even beat the times set up by No.1008 on the hills. What is significant, is that this was achieved at a cost in coal consumption, indeed the compounds burned as much coal in these tests as the 'Prince' had done the year before.

The new compounds with the larger cylinders were doing good work on the road, but on occasions when worked hard, the drivers were finding them short of steam. As a result, a further series of modifications were carried out and once again the Settle and Carlisle was the site for tests. No.1065 had the cylinders lined up to the Midland standard size, that is 19in. and 21in. and No.1060 had a new blastpipe fitted with the choke reduced from 4¾in. to 4½in. The results of these tests show how theory can be confounded by practice. The official report states that "No.1065 was able to work both the 300 ton and the 350 ton trains with less regulator and less cut-off than engine No.1060". The smaller cylinders seemed to have reduced the coal consumption a little, but it is asking too much to believe that they could increase the power output. Such are the vagaries of road tests.

It was in these tests that the examination of the work of No.1065 was subjected to the analysis by Mr. E. L. Diamond, referred to in the introduction.

As a result of the test, it was decided that the compound should become the main express locomotive for the whole LMS system, with the Midland control system extended to the other areas. However, having made this decision, it would seem that either someone had second thoughts, or that it was deemed necessary to justify the position, because yet another series of tests were set up in May 1925. This time, four locomotive classes were represented, a compound, again No.1065, a 'Claughton' No.30, *Thaiaba*, a Hughes class '8' and a 'Prince of Wales'. The compound was handled by Midland and the other three by North Western men, all from Carlisle and the route was between that city and Preston. The Hughes

4-6-0 made some very good times, especially on the climbs, but this was at the expense of high coal consumption. The North Western had not made the same mistake twice and the 'Claughton' was in first-rate condition and actually burned less coal per mile on some of the tests, than the compound. The 'Prince' was rather outclassed, but all the engines kept to the scheduled times on their runs. In the matter of coal per drawbar horsepower hour, the compound came out on top. Hauling trains of 350 tons the figures were:

Hughes class '8'	5.07lbs per D.H.P.
'Prince of Wales'	5.05lbs per D.H.P.
'Claughton'	4.78lbs per D.H.P.
Compound	4.25lbs per D.H.P.

In climbing Grayrigg and Shap, the compound was giving no one any points. In the case of the ascent of Shap, attacking the bank at a speed of 70m.p.h., speed had fallen to 25m.p.h. at the summit, but this gave a better time than any recorded by any North Western 4-4-0 similarly loaded. The maximum drawbar horsepower was 935 at a speed of 49m.p.h. Corrected for gradient, this works out at 1,330; indeed a remarkable performance.

Having had the point well and truly made, the LMS embarked on another flurry of compound building and within a year, another hundred had been added to the stock, built as follows:

1085-1114 Derby
1115-1134 Horwich
1135-1159 North British Loco
1160-1184 Vulcan Foundry.

There were now, at the end of 1925, 185 Midland compounds on the road and they were spread around the system thus: 20 in Scotland, 75 on the North Western and 90 on the Midland. There was then a pause in building for two years, but in 1927 another fifty were turned out by the Vulcan Foundry, Nos.1185-1199 and 900-934. At this time, there is reason to believe that the intention was to continue until there was a stock of at least three hundred compounds, but with the arrival of the 'Royal Scots', this was shelved. There was the strange case of the very last five compounds, built in 1932, Nos.935-939, which were originally intended to be built at Crewe, but finally appeared from Derby.

What then, of the everyday work of the compounds on the road? With the light Midland trains of the pre- and early post-grouping era, they were in the normal course of events, master of the tasks which were set. They provided the LMS and, indeed British Railways, with an efficient second-string passenger locomotive. It is,

A Fowler compound, No.1115. Built at Horwich in 1925.

however, difficult with the benefit of hindsight to imagine how the LMS operating authorities in the twenties thought they were going to haul the Anglo-Scottish traffic with such small locomotives. They were to be found all over the LMS, except at its northern and southern extremities, the Highland and the Somerset & Dorset. In the early 1930s, they took over almost all the local express passenger work on the former Caledonian and Glasgow & South Western lines; in 1933, there were 54 of them shared between nine sheds. They still worked some of the hardest turns, notably the 'Corridor' between Carlisle and Glasgow and the 'Postal' between Carlisle and Aberdeen.

Elsewhere, they worked all but the very heaviest expresses on their home ground on the former Midland main lines, including the West to North traffic from the Great Western and the cross-country traffic from Bristol to Birmingham. As more 4-6-0s were built, the compounds naturally became relegated more and more to secondary services, but the proudest moment came in April 1928, when No.1054 worked the Edinburgh portion of the 'Royal Scot' non-stop from Euston to the Scottish capital.

All the compounds survived to be taken into British Railways ownership, but withdrawal started in 1948 and several of the Midland locomotives not re-numbered in the 40000 series. These had all gone by the end of 1952 and a start had been made on the LMS series. The last of all, No.41168, went to the scrapyard in July 1961. Well, not quite the last, for of course, the very first one was retained for preservation by BR after withdrawal in October 1951. No.1000 was finally taken to Derby in 1959 and after much work, returned to steam. It had been considered that it might be possible to restore the locomotive to its original 1902 condition as No.2631, but this was not possible and the locomotive represents the engine as rebuilt in 1914.

Details of the Midland compounds

Midland Railway Locomotives

Number	Built	Superheated	Withdrawn
1000	1/1902	11/1914	10/1951
1001	1/1902	1/1915	11/1951
1002	7/1903	1/1919	6/1948
1003	9/1903	5/1915	4/1951
1004	11/1903	11/1914	2/1952
1005	10/1905	3/1923	7/1951
1006	11/1905	8/1922	5/1951
1007	11/1905	6/1922	5/1952
1008	11/1905	7/1919	7/1949
1009	12/1905	11/1922	3/1951
1010	12/1905	1/1927	7/1949
1011	12/1905	12/1922	2/1951
1012	12/1905	7/1921	1/1951
1013	12/1905	3/1925	6/1949
1014	12/1905	5/1919	5/1952
1015	3/1906	5/1921	12/1951
1016	3/1906	5/1922	11/1951
1017	3/1906	1/1926	8/1950
1018	4/1906	12/1926	7/1948
1019	4/1906	4/1924	12/1951
1020	4/1906	2/1922	5/1951
1021	4/1906	9/1927	10/1952
1022	5/1906	1/1928	4/1950
1023	5/1906	12/1922	8/1951
1024	5/1906	3/1922	10/1949
1025	5/1906	10/1924	1/1953
1026	6/1906	10/1927	9/1948
1027	6/1906	8/1926	10/1948
1028	6/1906	11/1923	10/1952
1029	7/1906	5/1924	6/1948
1030	9/1906	4/1925	9/1951
1031	9/1906	11/1922	12/1949
1032	10/1906	1/1926	3/1952
1033	10/1906	10/1923	9/1948
1034	12/1906	1/1923	5/1950
1035	11/1908	6/1922	5/1952

Midland Railway Locomotives *(continued)*

Number	Built	Superheated	Withdrawn
1036	11/1908	11/1923	10/1948
1037	12/1908	1/1921	3/1951
1038	12/1908	11/1922	8/1952
1039	12/1908	9/1920	6/1950
1040	1/1909	7/1913	5/1952
1041	1/1909	2/1923	12/1951
1042	2/1909	6/1920	6/1949
1043	3/1909	12/1925	13/1951
1044	3/1909	12/1926	10/1952

Before 1907 Nos.1000-1004 were 2631-2635.
Nos.1005-1034 were 1000-1029.

LMS Standard compounds

Number	Built	Withdrawn	Number	Built	Withdrawn
1045	2/1924	6/1957	1068	8/1924	12/1958
1046	2/1924	1/1953	1069	9/1924	12/1955
1047	2/1924	2/1924	1070	9/1924	12/1955
1048	3/1924	11/1957	1071	9/1924	3/1958
1049	3/1924	3/1959	1072	9/1924	11/1955
1050	3/1924	6/1956	1073	10/1924	9/1957
1051	3/1924	11/1954	1074	10/1924	8/1954
1052	4/1924	4/1953	1075	10/1924	4/1957
1053	4/1924	6/1956	1076	11/1924	5/1955
1054	4/1924	10/1954	1077	11/1924	4/1957
1055	4/1925	3/1053	1078	11/1924	9/1958
1056	5/1924	11/1953	1079	11/1924	11/1956
1057	5/1924	5/1953	1080	11/1924	1/1954
1058	5/1924	2/1954	1081	12/1924	12/1955
1059	6/1924	12/1955	1082	12/1924	4/1954
1060	6/1924	3/1958	1083	12/1924	12/1958
1061	6/1924	6/1955	1084	12/1924	6/1954
1062	6/1924	5/1959	1085	5/1925	1/1957
1063	7/1924	10/1960	1086	5/1925	5/1958
1064	7/1924	1/1957	1087	6/1925	11/1954
1065	7/1924	3/1956	1088	6/1925	12/1956
1066	8/1924	5/1958	1089	6/1925	7/1957
1067	8/1924	2/1955	1090	7/1925	12/1958

LMS Standard compounds *(continued)*

Number	Built	Withdrawn	Number	Built	Withdrawn
1091	7/1925	4/1955	1130	1/1926	9/1955
1092	7/1925	8/1953	1131	1/1926	3/1956
1093	7/1925	7/1958	1132	2/1926	10/1956
1094	7/1925	1/1959	1133	2/1926	10/1954
1095	8/1925	2/1958	1134	2/1926	10/1954
1096	8/1925	5/1954	1135	6/1925	9/1955
1097	8/1925	5/1956	1136	6/1925	10/1955
1098	8/1925	6/1957	1137	7/1925	4/1956
1099	9/1925	12/1953	1138	7/1925	12/1954
1100	9/1925	4/1959	1139	7/1925	10/1954
1101	9/1925	8/1959	1140	7/1925	5/1957
1102	10/1925	12/1958	1141	7/1925	9/1954
1103	10/1925	12/1957	1142	7/1925	7/1956
1104	10/1925	8/1955	1143	7/1925	3/1959
1105	11/1925	10/1957	1144	7/1925	3/1958
1106	11/1925	7/1958	1145	7/1925	10/1953
1107	11/1925	10/1955	1146	7/1925	11/1954
1008	11/1925	1/1957	1147	8/1925	3/1956
1109	12/1925	12/1952	1148	8/1925	3/1953
1110	12/1925	8/1954	1149	8/1925	8/1955
1111	12/1925	5/1958	1150	8/1925	10/1957
1112	12/1925	11/1957	1151	8/1925	1/1957
1113	12/1925	12/1958	1152	9/1925	3/1958
1114	12/1925	5/1958	1153	9/1925	11/1957
1115	6/1925	5/1954	1154	9/1925	8/1955
1116	7/1925	12/1957	1155	9/1925	3/1957
1117	8/1925	5/1955	1156	9/1925	9/1958
1118	8/1925	1/1958	1157	9/1925	5/1960
1119	9/1925	12/1958	1158	9/1925	9/1959
1120	10/1925	6/1959	1159	10/1925	4/1958
1121	10/1925	2/1959	1160	9/1925	10/1956
1122	11/1925	12/1958	1161	9/1925	12/1955
1123	11/1925	12/1959	1162	9/1925	6/1960
1124	11/1925	1/1955	1163	9/1925	12/1958
1125	12/1925	2/1953	1164	9/1925	11/1958
1126	12/1925	11/1956	1165	9/1925	3/1959
1127	12/1925	8/1955	1166	9/1925	10/1956
1128	12/1925	3/1956	1167	10/1925	11/1958
1129	12/1925	6/1955	1168	10/1925	7/1961

LMS Standard compounds *(continued)*

Number	Built	Withdrawn	Number	Built	Withdrawn
1169	10/1925	7/1955	1189	3/1927	7/1958
1170	11/1925	4/1956	1190	3/1927	1/1958
1171	11/1925	12/1952	1191	3/1927	3/1956
1172	11/1925	8/1957	1192	3/1927	6/1957
1173	11/1925	2/1959	1193	3/1927	11/1958
1174	11/1925	2/1954	1194	3/1927	9/1957
1175	11/1925	4/1955	1195	3/1927	12/1957
1176	11/1925	1/1955	1196	3/1927	7/1958
1177	11/1925	12/1955	1197	3/1927	5/1957
1178	11/1925	12/1953	1198	3/1927	12/1955
1179	12/1925	9/1957	1199	4/1927	1/1958
1180	12/1925	3/1957	900	4/1927	4/1956
1181	12/1925	11/1957	901	4/1927	6/1954
1182	12/1925	12/1952	902	4/1927	8/1956
1183	12/1925	2/1955	903	4/1927	9/1955
1184	12/1925	6/1953	904	4/1927	3/1957
1185	2/1927	11/1997	905	4/1927	12/1953
1186	2/1927	9/1957	906	4/1927	1/1955
1187	2/1927	7/1956	907	4/1927	10/1960
1188	3/1927	12/1955	908	5/1927	7/1955

Chapter 9
North British Railway

In 1871, Thomas Wheatley built two inside cylinder 4-4-0s, the first of this type to appear on a British standard gauge railway. They were fitted with inside frames, 17in. x 24in. cylinders and 6ft. 6in. driving wheels. On the night of 28th December 1879, the first of these, No.224 was the spare engine at Dundee, when the usual engine for the Up Night Mail train failed on shed. No.224 took the train to Burntisland and on the return, went down with the first Tay Bridge into the waters of the Firth. Early in 1880, she was lifted out and repaired and put back into service.

In 1885, Matthew Holmes rebuilt her as a four-cylinder tandem compound, on the system patented by W. H. Nesbit. The original cylinders were replaced by a pair of 20in. diameter, which sat over the centre of the bogie. In line with the front bogie wheels were a pair of high-pressure cylinders, 13in. in diameter and the stroke of all four remained at 24in.

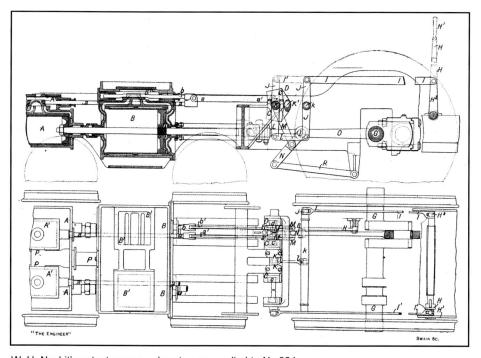

W. H. Nesbit's patent compound system as applied to No.224.

The locomotive worked for some years in this compound form, but nothing was published about the performance. It was later converted back to simple working and was withdrawn in 1919. Surely, a locomotive with more claim to fame than most!

North British 4-4-0 No.224, while working as a compound.

Chapter 10
London & North Eastern Railway

It is not surprising that a team, having just taken responsibility for the motive power for the whole of the new LNER and led by Nigel Gresley, should turn to unconventional means to improve the efficiency of that motive power. The appeal of high temperature and pressure in achieving this was obvious, but these presented two problems. Firstly, it was felt that the conventional locomotive boiler would become too heavy, both in weight and maintenance costs, if the pressure was taken much above 200p.s.i. and that, secondly, simple expansion would not be able to take advantage of the pressure range available.

In theory, an increase to a pressure of 450p.s.i. would give an improvement in thermal efficiency of at least 20% and Gresley had been giving much thought to the problems involved, even as far back as his Great Northern days. He eventually turned to marine practice as a method of keeping the weight of a boiler pressed to this figure within reasonable bounds. In conjunction with the firm of Yarrow of Glasgow, in September 1924, he began design work on the boiler, but such were the problems involved in fitting it onto a locomotive chassis, that over three years were to pass before a satisfactory solution was found. The boiler was ordered from Yarrow in 1928 and took over a year to complete. The concept was to produce a locomotive with equivalent power to the 'Pacifics' at work on the East Coast main line and tradition has it that the project was cloaked in such secrecy that the engine became known as 'Old Hush Hush'.

The Yarrow water tube reversed the normal system in which steam is raised in a locomotive boiler. Instead of a boiler filled with water through which passed fire tubes, there were five drums, a large one at the top and four smaller ones below, connected by banks of arched tubes, which held the water; the hot gases from the firebox played on these within the confines of the boiler casing. The upper drum, 3ft. feet in diameter, ran over the top of the firebox and was 28ft. long. Inside it, steam was collected in a perforated 5in. diameter pipe and carried to the superheater. The four lower drums were each in two pairs, 1ft. 6in. in diameter, the rear pair outside the firebox at the rear with the centres 7ft. 3in. apart and the forward running from the front of the firebox at 2ft. 3in. centres. The bank of tubes curved upwards and inwards between the drums and were 2½in. diameter at the rear and 2in. diameter at the front of the boiler. The casing was fabricated from sheet and was shaped like a triangle with rounded angles when viewed from the front, or rear. The external size decreased forward in three steps.

To take advantage of the high boiler pressure, the locomotive was built as a four-

Gresley's 'Hush Hush' compound No.10000 approaching Darlington in June 1930 with an up express.

cylinder compound and the cylinders were arranged in the de Glehn manner and the drive was divided. The inside, high-pressure cylinders were 12in. diameter and the low-pressure 20in. After some trials, it was found that the distribution of work was uneven, so the high-pressure diameter was reduced to 10in. Two sets of outside Walschaerts gear were fitted and the high-pressure valves were driven through rocking levers. These were arranged so that the cut-off could be adjusted independently by means of a slotted die block. A conventional locomotive chassis, similar to the standard 'Pacifics' was used, but to carry the extra length, a bissel truck was fitted behind the rear carrying wheels, thus producing a 4-6-2-2, although she was usually referred to as a 4-6-4.

No.10000 was sent to Gateshead in the summer of 1930 and worked alongside the normal 'Pacifics' and, in a paper read to the Institute of Mechanical Engineers in January 1931, Gresley reported that initial trials had been successfully completed. This paper gave comprehensive technical data. In normal working, the locomotive gave every appearance of coming up to expectations. The roster included the long mileage day, starting with Newcastle to Edinburgh, returning with the Glasgow to Leeds diner as far as York and then back to Newcastle. The southbound run included the usual fast timing from Darlington to York in 43 minutes for the 44 miles. In July 1930, No.10000 worked the non-stop 'Flying Scotsman' from King's Cross to Edinburgh and back on successive days. On the timing then in force, this presented no problem, but the average speed demanded was no more than 46 miles per hour. The actual handling of the locomotive turned out to be quite tricky; particular difficulty was experienced in keeping the boiler pressure at a constant level. What is more, the engine turned out to be weak when working compound. Even more serious was the problem of keeping the boiler casing airtight. As railway engineers have found since, the pounding of a steel wheel on a steel rail is a very unforgiving and punishing action and the casing joints developed leaks leading to serious heat loss. This led to very high maintenance costs and, as the years went by, No.10000 did less and less work. Finally, in 1937, Gresley decided to rebuild her as a conventional three-cylinder simple with an 'A4' casing and derived motion. In this form, she ran, finally as British Railway No.60700, until withdrawn in 1959.

Four-cylinder compound No.10000
Built Doncaster 1929.
Rebuilt as three-cylinder simple 1937.
Withdrawn as class 'W1' No. 60700 1959.

A detailed view of the casing covering the unique Yarrow water tube boiler.

Chapter 11

Great Central Railway

In the years after the completion of the London Extension into Marylebone, the Great Central had to compete with the established lines to the North. To do this some very fast schedules were put on but the loads were very light and the Pollitt 'Singles' and Robinson's 4-4-0s were quite capable of keeping time. The railway was, as ever, ambitious and in 1903, Robinson ordered four ten wheel express locomotives from Beyer, Peacock & Co. Two of these were 'Atlantics' and two 4-6-0 and were mechanically similar apart from the wheel arrangement. The 'Atlantics' would appear to have found favour because no more of this particular class (GCR 8c) of 4-6-0s were built but a further twenty of the 4-4-2s were built by Beyer, Peacock, The North British Locomotive Company, and five at the railway's own works at Gorton. An additional four were built at Gorton in 1905 and 1906 as three cylinder Smith compounds.

The compounds had the cylinders set in the standard Smith arrangement with the single, 19in. high pressure inside and the two 21in. low pressure outside. The common stroke was 26in. The drive was divided with the high pressure cylinder driving the leading coupled axle. The valve were actuated by three sets of Stephenson Link motion between the frames. The driving wheel diameter was 6ft. 9in.

As originally built without superheaters, the boilers contained 221 tubes giving a heating surface of 1778sq.ft. to which the firebox added 153sq.ft. The pressure was originally 200p.s.i. When the boilers were superheated the pressure was reduced to 180p.s.i. The grate area was 26sq.ft. The weight of the engine in working order was 71 tons of which 37 tons resting on the driving wheels.

It was difficult to distinguish the compound 'Atlantics' from the simples except for the numbers and the fact that the compounds carried names, but it has long

Great Central compound 'Atlantic' No.258.

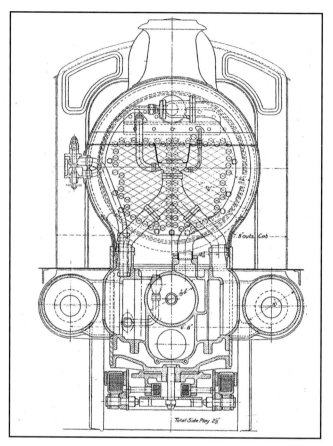

Cylinder and smokebox arrangement of the Robinson 3-cylinder compound 'Atlantic'.

been acknowledged that these were among the most handsome of all British steam locomotives. They were known as 'Jersey Lillies' and as this was also the nickname of one of the great stage beauties of the time, Lilly Langtry, it was thought that the grace and beauty of the one was transferred to the other. It now appears that nothing could be further from the truth. At the time of the delivery of the first 'Atlantics' from Beyer's works, there was a great deal of comment on their size and particularly the large diameter boiler as compared with older Great Central locomotives. At the same time, there was on exhibition at a local pub near the Gorton works an extremely large woman, reputed to weigh 500 pounds and sarcastically advertised as the 'Jersey Lilly'. This led to someone at the works naming the locomotive 'Jersey Lilly' and the name has stuck ever since.

On the road the performance was as impressive as the looks but in the early days the loads were generally so light as not to tax the power of the 'Atlantics'. It was later, under LNER ownership, like their Great Northern, equivalents that their glory days came. The most demanding work after the grouping came on the down expresses from Marylebone like the 6.20p.m. to Bradford. This was exclusively an 'Atlantic' job for some years and the compounds took their turn. The train was routed via High Wycombe because of the heavy 'home going' commuter traffic on the other, Metropolitan, route at that time in the evening. The schedule allowed a time of 114 minutes for the 107.6 miles non stop to Leicester. Two slip coaches were carried, one detached at Finmere and the other at Woodford to provide a service to Stratford on Avon. The schedule had originally been planned for a load of about 200 tons but the train had now grown so that 300 tons was the norm and given the adverse gradients and the speed restrictions at Neasden, Northolt and through the old station at High Wycombe, to pass Princes Risborough, 36 miles, in 45 minutes demanded work of the highest order. This left 69 minutes for the remaining 71 miles and it was not unusual to achieve three 'eighties' in the course of this run.

The four compounds outlasted the Second World War but were scrapped in 1946 and 1947 and so failed to come under British Railways ownership.

Robinson 3 cylinder Compound Atlantics.

Great Central Class 8D & 8E

LNER Class C5

Built 1905 - 1906   Gorton Works.

Last locomotive withdrawn 1947

5258   *The Rt. Hon. Viscount Cross, G.C.B.,G.C.S.I.*
5259   *King Edward VII*
5364   *Lady Faringdon*
5365   *Sir William Pollitt*

Chapter 12

Ireland

In 1883, John Aspinal, then of the Great Southern & Western Railway and formerly a pupil at Crewe, applied to his Board of Directors for permission to build a locomotive of the Webb three-cylinder compound type. Largely because the cost of the compounds was £250 more for each locomotive, this was refused and four express simples built instead. But, following the construction of the type described below, Harry Ivatt, on the same railway in 1894, was sufficiently impressed by the performance of the compounds to convert one of Aspinal 4-4-0s into a two-cylinder compound. The cylinders were 18in. and 26in. in diameter, with a common stroke of 24in. and the boiler pressure remained at 150p.s.i. The starting valve was operated by the driver to admit steam directly into the low-pressure cylinder and was non-automatic. The engine was not a success. The exhaust became choked by the high volume of the exhaust from the low-pressure cylinder and the valve was a continual source of trouble. Rebuilding as a two-cylinder simple took place in 1901.

It is strange that, just at the time that two-cylinder compound locomotives were being replaced, or rebuilt in England, the type should make its appearance on the other side of the Irish Sea. In 1890, new locomotives were ordered by B. Malcolm of the Belfast & Northern Counties Railway from Beyer Peacock. Herman Lange of that firm suggested two-cylinder compounds and his suggestion was accepted. Four locomotives to the Beyer Peacock design were delivered to York Road, Belfast in April, May and July 1890 and known as Class 'C'. They were 2-4-0s, with 6ft. diameter driving wheels and leading wheels of 4ft. 1¾in. The two inside cylinders, 16in. and 23¼in. in diameter, with a common stroke of 24in. were fed by slide valves actuated by Walschaerts valve gear. This was only the second use of this gear in a British locomotive, although Beyer Peacock had built many locomotives for overseas railways fitted with it. The valve gear was arranged to give a cut-off about 2% later in the low-pressure cylinder than in the high-pressure. This factor certainly contributed to the relative success of all the Irish two-cylinder compounds. The boiler was 4ft. 1in. in diameter and had a total heating surface of 850sq.ft. The boiler pressure was 170p.s.i. and the weight, of the locomotive alone, was 37 tons 6cwt. The starting system used the Von Borries disc intercepting valve, which allowed live steam into both cylinders for the first stroke only, after which the valve opened and full compound working commenced. There were eventually seven of these locomotives, Nos.21, 33, 51, 56, 57 and 58 and they were a success on the road. They had long and varied lives, some being rebuilt as two-cylinder simples and some being withdrawn as compounds. Following the purchase in 1903 of the railway by the Midland Railway of England, standard Derby boilers were used in the rebuildings. By 1937, only No.56 was in its original condition and was withdrawn in 1942. No.21 (by then renumbered 51) and No.57 were still running as compounds, but rebuilt with Derby G6 boilers and leading bogies. The other four were all rebuilt as two-cylinder simples. No.33 ran with the name *Galgorm Castle*, the home of the General Manager, John Young. In 1892, there was a further order to Beyer Peacock for two 0-6-0 goods engines. Class 'E', with 5ft. 2½in. driving wheels. They were delivered in April and May 1892 at a cost of £2736 each. The boiler was slightly larger than that fitted to the Class 'C', with 980sq.ft. of heating surface; the mechanics were similar, except that larger cylinders, 18in. and 26in. in diameter and again with 24in. stroke, were fitted. In the event, these were reduced to 17in. and 25in. before delivery. They proved rather unhandy in service and were rebuilt as two-cylinder simples with 18in. x 26in. cylinders and G6 boilers, No.54 in 1907 and No.53 in 1911. They were finally withdrawn in 1934 and 1944.

In June 1895, Beyer Peacock delivered two larger 2-4-0 compounds, class 'D' with 7ft. diameter driving wheels. They were mechanically similar to the earlier class, but with larger 18in. and 26in. diameter cylinders and a 4ft. 4in. boiler with 940sq.ft. of heating surface. They were inclined to 'hunt' at speed and were soon rebuilt as 4-4-0s with a standard Beyer Peacock bogie. In this form, they weighed 46 tons 9cwt. No.50 *Jubilee* was rebuilt as a two-cylinder simple with 19in. x 24in. cylinders in 1926 and withdrawn in 1946. No.55 *Parkmont* ran as a compound until withdrawal in 1944.

Belfast & Northern Counties Railway class 'D' No.50 *Jubilee*.

In 1897, another five compounds were bought from Manchester, class 'B', similar to class 'C', except for the leading bogie with 3ft. diameter wheels. Of these, two locomotives, Nos.60 and 61, were fitted in 1921 with the G6 boiler, but continued to run as compounds until 1932, when they were rebuilt as two-cylinder simples. Both were withdrawn in 1946. Three more, Nos.24, 51 and 58, were also fitted with the G6 boiler in 1924, but were rebuilt as simples with 18in. x 24in. cylinders at the same time. The remaining two, Nos.59 and 62, received the superheated G7 boiler and the same size cylinders, also in 1924. For some time, No.59 ran with a modified starting valve to allow live steam to be fed to the low-pressure cylinder while running, but this proved to be too great a drain on the boiler and was removed.

The final class of two-cylinder compounds were all built at the York Road works in Belfast to the same general design. They had the 6ft. driving wheels of Class 'C', combined with the 18in. and 26in. cylinders of class 'D'. Classified as 'A', the delivery was spread out over the years 1901-1908 and there were eight locomotives in the class. They were gradually rebuilt from 1925 onwards with G7 superheated boilers and 18in x 24in. cylinders. The last to run as a compound was No.63 which was rebuilt in 1936. In their simple form, most of them lasted into the 1950s. In addition to the standard gauge locomotives, Beyer Peacock designed a series of 3ft.-gauge compound tank engines for the Belfast & Northern Counties. The first two were built in Manchester in 1892 and five more were built at York Road. They were 2-4-2 side tanks, with driving wheels 3ft. 9in. in diameter, the radial wheels being 2ft. and having outside bearings. The boiler, 3ft. 5in. in diameter, had a heating surface of 741sq.ft. and carried a pressure of 160p.s.i.. The two outside cylinders were 14¾in. and 21in. diameter with a stroke of 20in. Outside Walschaerts motion drove slide valves. The tanks, which extended to the front of the smokebox, held 570 gallons of water and the bunker carried one ton of coal. They weighed 33 tons. In 1931, No.110 was rebuilt, under the superintendence of W. P. Stewart, as a 2-4-4, leading to an increase in the coal capacity, which now

Belfast & Northern Counties Railway 3ft. gauge compound 2-4-2T.

became 1½ tons. A modified Midland G6S Belpaire boiler was fitted with a pressure of 200p.s.i.; this increased the weight to 44 tons. The extended wheelbase, with no less than 9ft. 6in. between the rear driving wheels and the leading bogie wheels, proved to be far too long and rigid for the curves on the narrow gauge. The rebuild was an almost total failure and only ran 60,000 miles in its new guise, before withdrawal in 1946. The others were slowly withdrawn as the narrow-gauge mileage reduced, the last being No.111, which was renumbered 44 in 1948 and ran until the Ballycastle Railway was closed in June 1950.

In 1892, at the same time that Beyer Peacock were building the class 'C' compounds for the Belfast & Northern Counties, they supplied three identical 2-4-0 compounds to the Belfast & County Down Railway. At the same time, they built four 2-4-2 tank engines with larger, 18in. and 26in. diameter cylinders and 5ft. driving wheels. The boiler was also larger, with a heating surface of 1,163sq.ft. and a grate area of 19sq.ft. They weighed 56½ tons. They proved rather unstable in their original form and in 1894, three of the four were rebuilt with a leading bogie. Even this was not a total success and over the next few years they were rebuilt as two-cylinder simples. They were all scrapped by 1920.

Belfast & County Down Railway compound 2-4-2T of 1892.

In the early 1930s, the Irish Railways and in particular the Great Northern (Ireland), were caught up in the quest for more speed. The most important route was that between Belfast and Dublin and, with the loads reaching 300 tons, the two-cylinder 4-4-0s then in use were being overwhelmed by the current schedules, let alone those proposed. The problem which stood in the way of more powerful locomotives was, as ever, weight. There were two viaducts on the line which would need strengthening before higher axle loads could be permitted, the Boyne Viaduct at Drogheda and that at nearby Malahide and this work was taken in hand in 1931. Colonel George Glover, who had been locomotive engineer at Dundalk since 1912, was fortunate in having the report of the Bridge Stress Committee to put before his Civil Engineer and, as a result of this, was allowed an axle load of 21 tons for a well balanced, multi-cylinder locomotive. It has been said that the Maunsell 'Schools' were the ultimate in 4-4-0 design, but the Glover three-cylinder compounds of 1932 must be admitted to run them pretty close.

In essence, the five 'V' class were a modern version of the standard Midland compound and Glover acknowledged the help he received from Derby and from Sir Henry Fowler and Sir Ernest Lemon in the design of the locomotives which were built by Beyer Peacock at Manchester; the tenders were built at the railway works at Dundalk. The boiler was somewhat smaller than had been thought necessary earlier in the twentieth century for the work expected of the locomotives, but Glover, like Nigel Gresley in the 'D49' class, expected full use to be made of the large range of expansion available with high-pressure, high superheated steam and modern valve settings. The barrel was 5ft. 1¼in. in diameter and 11ft. 4in. between the tubeplates, This gave a heating surface of 1,251sq.ft. and a large Robinson type superheated added a further 276sq.ft. The boiler pressure of 250p.s.i. was the highest carried by a 4-4-0 in these islands.

The three cylinders were arranged in the Smith fashion, with one high-pressure, 17¼in. in diameter, inside and two low-pressure, 19in. in diameter, outside. The common stroke was 26in. All three cylinders drove on the leading coupled axle and three sets of link motion were fitted, all inside. The steam distribution was by a piston valve for the high-pressure side and balanced slide valves for the two low-pressure cylinders, but these proved troublesome and were replaced by ordinary flat

The now preserved class 'V' 4-4-0 No.85 *Merlin* as running in May 2003.

valves in 1933. To obtain an even turning moment and better balancing, the two low-pressure cranks were set at 90 degrees to each other and the high-pressure at 135 degrees to them. The starting system was borrowed from Derby in that the Deeley regulator was used. The coupling rods between the 6ft. 7in. driving wheels were 10ft. 8in. long. This enabled a long, flat grate to be fitted between the axles, making the fireman's task much easier. The total weight of the locomotive was 65 tons and of the tender, with 6 tons of coal and 3,500 gallons of water, 38 tons. The five locomotives were numbered and named:

83 *Eagle*
84 *Falcon*
85 *Merlin*
86 *Peregrine*
87 *Kestrel*

The introduction of these locomotives enabled the schedules to be cut dramatically. The times were cut by 14 minutes Northbound and 22 minutes Southbound to 2 hours 28 minutes and 2 hours 27 minutes respectively. These included a stop of about 8 minutes at the border between Ulster and the Republic for Customs inspection and the running time of two hours nine minutes was just under the present, diesel hauled, non-stop time. The 3.15p.m. Down service included the first 60 miles per hour start to stop run in Ireland. Several published runs show the capabilities of the locomotives. One example will suffice. On a service run, No.86 *Peregrine*, maintained 74m.p.h. on level track, with a load of 300 tons and a maximum of 85m.p.h. on a 1:200 descent. With a reduced load of 230 tons, a speed of 40m.p.h. was held up the 1:125 of Adavoyle Bank. Coal consumption on the hardest runs was said to be a moderate 39- 45 pounds per train mile. This sort of performance goes some way to showing what a compound could achieve with high-pressure and a modern front end. After Glover's retirement in 1934, the boiler pressure was reduced to 200p.s.i., because the timings were eased and some of the sparkle went out of the work. Nevertheless, the compounds were found to be capable of handling loads of 400 tons on the Belfast-Dublin run, unassisted except for banking on the worst part of Adavoyle. They were rebuilt with new Belpaire boilers carrying 215p.s.i. in 1946-7. In 1948, some similar locomotives were built, save that they were three-cylinder simples.

The compounds must rank among the success stories of locomotive design. They were fast and powerful and capable of doing the job they were built for. Midland Railway enthusiasts may have looked wistfully across the Irish Sea and thought that these were the locomotives that Henry Fowler should have built in 1923.

Chapter 13

Miscellaneous

Blyth & Tyne Railway
0-6-0 Built August 1868.
Three-cylinders: 2 outside 10in. x 24in. (with cranks moving in unison)
                 1 inside 20in. x 24in.
Driving Wheels 4ft. 6in.
There is some doubt about this locomotive and although some authorities say that it was a compound, it is probable that it was a three-cylinder simple. The locomotive became North Eastern No.1335.

Charles Burrell & Sons
Two 3ft. 6in. gauge tram engines, one built in 1885, works No.1119, for the Bradford & Shelf Tramway and one in 1886, works No.1190, for Birmingham Central Tramways.
0-4-0 Driving wheels 2ft. 6in.
Two-cylinders 10in. x 14in. high-pressure
              17½in. x 14in. low-pressure
Boiler pressure 160p.s.i.
Joy valve gear.
They were fitted with a condenser of a new type in which air was passed over both inner and outer surfaces of the exhaust steam pipe.

J.& H. McLaren, Leeds
Traction Engine type. Works No.1547.
For Hall & Son, Croydon.
0-4-0 Driving Wheels 3ft 1in.
Two-cylinders 6½in. x 12in. high-pressure
              10¾in. x 12in. low-pressure

Thomas Robinson & Son Ltd., Rochdale
0-4-0 Two-cylinder *Mary*.
Vertical boiler.

Saville Street Foundry, Sheffield.
Built 1882. Given trial on Burnley Tramways.
Tramway Type
Two-cylinders 8in. x 14in. high pressure
              12in x 14in. low pressure.

Chapter 14
Unbuilt Compounds

Given the relative and perceived success of the Johnson/Deeley compounds on the Midland, it is not surprising that other compound locomotives were considered. In 1905, Deeley's fertile mind came up with an extraordinary design for a four-cylinder compound tank engine. The boiler was to be identical with the saturated 4-4-0 compounds, with a pressure of 220p.s.i. and a grate area of 28.4sq.ft. Below the platforms, the arrangement was very unconventional. The wheel arrangement was 2-4-4-2, with two sets of uncoupled driving wheels, with the high-pressure cylinders, 13in. diameter and 26in. stroke, driving the rear pair from behind. The low-pressure cylinders, 20in. diameter and 26in. stroke, drove the front pair. The driving wheel diameter was to be 5ft. Steam distribution was to be by Walschearts gear and the high-pressure cylinders were to be fitted with piston valves and the low-pressure with slide valves. The leading and trailing wheels, 3ft. 3in. diameter, were to be carried on Bissel Trucks and the wheel base of 37ft. was to be rigid. Water capacity was to be 2000 gallons, mostly in long side tanks, with a small bunker tank and 3½ tons of coal were to be carried. The weight, in working order, was to have been 89 tons.

It has been suggested (by Hamilton Ellis in 'The Midland Railway') that this design was Deeley's response to Paget's extraordinary 2-6-2. In any case, it is difficult to imagine what sort of work Deeley was considering for this locomotive. The driving wheel size indicates fast freight work, as the long coupled wheel base and Bissel trucks would not produce the most stable platform for high speed. There are other obvious questions over the design. The position of the high-pressure cylinders resulted in very long steam pipes, outside and even longer pipes from the high-pressure exhaust to the low-pressure receiver. If the standard Deeley starting system was used, with his design of regulator, the rear driving wheels would not be driven at first and this would, inevitably, cause considerable resistance. The design drawing is dated 11th December 1905 and, given that the memory of the Webb compounds, with their uncoupled driving wheels, would be quite fresh, it would take a very brave designer to repeat the experiment. Of course, in this case, each pair of driving wheels were coupled, but each pair would be just as likely to slip and lack of synchronisation was inevitable.

Almost the last of Deeley's designs, before his precipitant departure from the Midland Railway, was for a four-cylinder compound 4-6-0. The drawings for this locomotive are dated 26th November 1907 and, if it had been built, would have brought the Midland into the forefront of express passenger operation, well ahead of all the railways on the East and West Coast main lines and up there with the latest Swindon products. The cylinder arrangement was to have been on the de Glehn lines with the high-pressure outside fitted between the rear of the bogie and the front driving wheels. The valve gear, inside, was the famous 'Scissors' motion which caused such friction between Deeley and Churchward and all the cylinders were to be fitted with 8¾in. piston valves. The outside valves were to be driven by rocking shafts.

The boiler was to be a straightforward enlargement of the 4-4-0 compound boiler, with a heating surface of 1,970sq.ft. and a grate area of 30sq.ft. At this time, of course, the Midland operation was being re-organised by Paget and it may be that this locomotive did not fit into the pattern of light and frequent trains which he came up with. The story, again related by Hamilton Ellis, is that Deeley stormed into the works at Derby one morning, accompanied by a workman and incandescent with rage. The workman removed Deeley's name from his office door and he left the works and railway work for ever. So, his great locomotive was never built and the Midland never produced an express engine larger than the 4-4-0 compounds.

One compound which never even reached the design stage was the result of the conversion of Churchward's 'Pacific' *The Great Bear* into a 'Castle'. Although this locomotive had long been considered something of a 'white elephant' by the operating department of the Great Western, it was still thought of as a prestige symbol by the senior management, particularly by the General Manager, Sir Felix Pole. When, in 1926, the Southern Railway announced the introduction of the *Lord Nelson*, 'the most powerful passenger engine in Great Britain' based on its tractive effort of 33,500lbs., Collett was instructed to produce a locomotive to re-establish the pre-eminence of Swindon. Pole was amazed to learn that it could not be done, because the 'Castle' had been designed right up to the limit which the Civil Engineer would accept. However, Stanier and Hawksworth had been working on a proposal which would have met the requirement. The idea was for a compound 'Castle' based on the best de Glehn concepts. The outline was made by Hawksworth and with high-pressure cylinders 17in. diameter and low-pressure of 25in., the tractive effort came out at 33,700lbs. An adjustment to the 'Castle' wheelbase was necessary, which involved moving the bogie centre forward by about 2ft., but the drawings produced a typical, neat Churchward outline. They decided the time was ripe to approach Collett with the proposal. As Hawksworth told O. S. Nock, "We went in to see him and in about five minutes we were out again". And that was that!

The grouping of the railways of Britain into the 'Big Four' in 1923 produced much turmoil and denting of egos. Nowhere was this more true than in the locomotive department of the LMS. The first Chief Mechanical Engineer of the new Company was George Hughes, who came to the post via the amalgamation the previous year of the LNWR and the Lancashire & Yorkshire. There were two large 4-6-0s designed in existence. The first was his own, '5P' class and the other was the 'Claughton' of the LNWR. The original '5P' was as near to a total failure as any major class of passenger locomotive before or since and, even after rebuilding, had a prodigious appetite for coal. Operating the 'Claughton' has been described as "putting to sea in a sieve". Some measure of sanity returned to the department after Sir Henry Fowler succeeded Hughes in 1925 and he moved the headquarters to Derby. It was obvious to Fowler that there would be a requirement for a large, modern express passenger locomotive, although the operating department, organised on Paget's Midland system, had shown no desire for this. Fowler's office came up with a design for an enlargement of the Johnson/Deeley compound with a 4-6-0 wheel arrangement. The outline drawing shows a locomotive totally in the Derby tradition; it is clearly recognisable as a 'stretched' 4-4-0, even to the shape of the cab, firebox and splashers. Except in the use of outside Walscherts gear and, as a result, placing the outside valves above the cylinders, the engine layout closely followed that of the 4-4-0s. The drive was on the leading couple axle and the wheelbase, with 8ft. 3in. between the rear bogie wheel and the front driver, was exactly the same. The cylinders were, however, to be much larger with the high-pressure one 20¼in. diameter and the two low-pressure 22¼in.; the stroke in both cases a very long 30in. With the standard compound pressure of 220p.s.i., the boiler was no less than 16ft. 6in. This compares with 14ft. on the 'Royal Scot'. Despite this, the weight was less than the 'Scot'. Whether the performance of this locomotive would have come up to expectations is very much open to question, as Derby was still wedded to the 'Short Lap, Short Travel' valve gear and the notoriously inadequate bearing surfaces.

At the time when the design of the 4-6-0 was coming to fruition, E. L. Diamond, who was on the staff at Derby, read a paper to the Institute of Mechanical Engineers which, literally, rocked the established concepts of locomotive design back on their heels. Diamond, who at the time was on the design staff at Derby, had carried out his research privately in order to present this paper. It is worth quoting his ideas behind this project in full:

'The object of this investigation is to ascertain what proportions of the available energy of the steam between boiler and atmospheric pressures are accounted for by the various known sources of loss in the engine and to discover the relationship between the variation of these losses and the conditions under which they occur. It is necessarily confined to the study of one particular locomotive but the results herein set forth should be regarded as an indication of an extensive field of research'.

The locomotive in question was the 4-4-0 compound No.1065 and the test took place between Leeds and Carlisle. What Diamond found was that, even with a relatively efficient locomotive as the compound, at higher speeds, in this case 68m.p.h., while the engine developed 800 horsepower used in useful work to haul the train, 200 horsepower was lost in throttling at valve admission and another 200 horsepower in exhaust throttling and back pressure. These losses were much lower at low speeds. Diamond went on to say:

'It is, perhaps, not without significance that the one British railway company which has standardised the long lap valve for years past is the railway whose main line is level and whose trains are scheduled at the highest average speed'.

The impact at Derby was immediate. Fowler scrapped the valve gear on the newest engines then on the drawing board, the '2300' class of 2-6-4 tanks and stopped all work on the proposed 4-6-0 compound.

At the same meeting of the Institute and as part of the discussion of Diamond's paper, Breville, Chief Mechanical Engineer of the 'Nord' in France, provided details of tests carried out on the de Glehn 4-cylinder compound 'Pacifics', which were doing outstanding work on that railway. These showed that with high-pressure, independent cut-offs and long travel, long lap valves, many of the losses identified in Diamond's tests could be eliminated. Fowler visited France at this time to see the new compounds at work.

On his return, he started work on a new design for a compound 'Pacific'. This incorporated all the features of the de Glehn locomotives, except independent cut-offs. It was still thought that the skill level of the average British driver was not high enough to take advantage of this feature. The design work was split between the LMS works. The cylinders and valve gear was given to Horwich and only two sets of Walschearts motion was provided, with the inside valves actuated by rocking levers. Chambers, at Derby, was given responsibility for the boiler and the detailed work was carried out at Crewe. The design was presented to the LMS Locomotive Committee and Fowler was given the go-ahead to produce two locomotives. Work was started and even got as far as cutting the frames. At this point, the 'small engine' cabal of the operating division took a hand. Without Fowler's knowledge, it was arranged to borrow a 'Castle' from the GWR and test runs were made between Euston and Crewe and Crewe to Carlisle. Except for some problems with sanding in the North, the Great Western engine covered itself with glory. After an abortive attempt to buy some 'Castles', and with some help from the Southern Railway, which provided drawings of the 'Lord Nelson', an order was placed for fifty locomotives from the North British Locomotive Company. The 'Royal Scot' was born and all work on Fowler's great 'Pacific' was cancelled.

Bibliography

A.H Ahrons: The British Steam Locomotive 1825 -1925

O.S Nock: Locomotives of the North Eastern Railway
The Midland Compounds
Atlantic Locomotives
British Locomotives of the 20th Century

E.T MacDermot: History of the Great Western Railway

Hamilton Ellis: The Midland Railway

The Locomotive Magazine

The Engineer Magazine

R C T S: The L.N.W.R Eight Coupled Goods Engines
Locomotives of the L.S.W.R

W.A. Tuplin: North Eastern Steam